Town and Gov

THE HORN OF PLENTY

77 Lord Nuffield's benefactions to the university, 1936: cartoon.
By courtesy of *Punch*.

Town and Gown

Eight Hundred Years of Oxford Life

An Exhibition at the Bodleian Library, Oxford 1982

BUCKLER DRAWINGS

A group of ten early nineteenth-century Oxford views are hung on the panelling of the exhibition room. They are all by John Chessell Buckler (1793 - 1894).

1. A view in St. Ebbe's Street looking towards the church of St. Peter le Bailey, 1821. The church which jutted out into Queen Street was pulled down in 1874.

2. A view looking west down Ship Street towards Cornmarket, 1828.

3. New Carfax church at the corner of Queen Street and Cornmarket, 1821. The church, just built when this drawing was made, was pulled down in 1896.

4. Houses adjoining the Town Hall, St. Aldates, seen from Queen Street, 1827.

5. Nixon's School, behind the Old Town Hall, 1825. It was pulled down in 1896.

6. The view looking north from the junction of Cornmarket and Broad Street, 1823.

7. The courtyard of the Greyhound Inn which stood on the east corner of the junction of Longwall Street and the High Street, 1827.

8. Old houses on the north side of George Street, 1821. The Apollo Theatre now stands on this site.

9. A scene in Queen Street where the Westgate shopping centre is now, 1824.

10. Folly Bridge from the east, 1827.

Town and Gown

*

EIGHT HUNDRED YEARS
OF OXFORD LIFE

1982

AN EXHIBITION AT
THE BODLEIAN LIBRARY, OXFORD

ISBN O 900177 85 3

Supported by the English Tourist Board
through the Special Promotions Programme

FRONT COVER AND HALF TITLE:
caricatures by Robert Dighton (1752–1814)

FRONT COVER:
William Hall, brewer, of the Swan Brewery, Oxford, 1807;
'A view taken at Oxford', of an unidentified don, 1808.

HALF TITLE:
Alderman William Fletcher, 'Father of the Corporation', 1808;
'A view from Jesus College, Oxford', of
Dr David Hughes, Principal of the College, 1808.

Printed in Great Britain at the Alden Press, Oxford

CONTENTS

SPONSORS

City of Oxford
Oxford Preservation Trust
English Tourist Board
(through the Special Promotions Programme)
BBC Radio Oxford

BUSINESS FIRMS

Art Needlework Industries Limited
Barclays Bank Limited, Old Bank
B. H. Blackwell Limited
British Rail, Oxford Area
British Telecommunications
Buckell & Ballard (Oxford)
City of Oxford Taxicab Association
Cole & Cole
R. B. Cole Esq.
Frank Cooper (CPC (United Kingdom) Limited)
E. H. Crapper Esq.
Gill & Co. (Ironmongers) Limited
Halls Oxford & West Brewery Company Limited
G. T. Jones & Co.
Linnell & Murphy
Mallams
Morrell's Brewery Limited
A. R. Mowbray & Co. Limited
Payne & Son (Goldsmiths) Limited
Post Office, Oxford
Savory's
Shepherd & Woodward Limited
Stephenson & Co. (Oxford) Limited
Symm & Co. Limited
Thornton Baker

Walters & Co. (Oxford) Limited
Williams & Glyn's Bank Limited

*

Christ Church Cathedral School
Magdalen College School
New College School
Oxford University, Department
for External Studies
The Master, St. Peter's College
The Master, University College

*

THE GOVERNING BODIES OF —

All Souls College
Balliol College
Christ Church
Exeter College
Jesus College
Linacre College
Lincoln College
Magdalen College
Merton College
Nuffield College
Oriel College
Pembroke College
The Queen's College
St. Hugh's College
St. John's College
Somerville College
Trinity College
Wadham College
Worcester College

INTRODUCTION

The history of the relationship between a city whose origins go back to Saxon times and a university which has been growing in its centre since at least the early twelfth century is a long and complicated one. This exhibition, which is limited by available space to some 173 items, cannot hope to cover all aspects of that relationship, and it has therefore aimed to illustrate some of them and to show, by means primarily of documents and books from the Bodleian Library, Oxfordshire County Libraries, Oxford University Archives, and Oxford City Archives, how the two groups of people and their governing bodies have interacted over the centuries.

No one would claim that town and gown have dwelt harmoniously together at all times. Further, it is a fact that the contents of muniment rooms have a built-in bias. It is the periods of discord, of dispute, and of violence which produce written evidence: rarely does harmony leave its mark in the archives, still less in newspapers, periodicals, and pamphlets. If, however, many of these exhibits are the documentary results of dispute, what they show is that, from the twelfth to the twentieth century, city and university have been mutually dependent, and that the increasing economic independence which the city has achieved in this century has led not to less but to more cooperation.

The exhibition is divided into three broad sections: the first deals with some aspects of the physical growth of the city and the university, the second with the history of town and gown relationships, and the third with aspects of community life. Within these general sections the catalogue divides the exhibits into eight subsections and provides a short introduction to each.

The idea for this exhibition was first put forward by Dr Frank Garside during his year as Sheriff of Oxford, and, following two meetings of interested parties, the Bodleian Library agreed to mount it and a working group was set up to plan likely themes, select potential exhibits, and draft a catalogue. The brunt of this work was borne by Miss Ruth Vyse of Oxford University Archives, who was assisted by Steven Tomlinson of the Department of Western Manuscripts at the Bodleian Library, and Malcolm Graham of Oxfordshire County Libraries. Much help was also generously given by Alan Crossley, editor of the Victoria County History of Oxfordshire, and Dan Chadwick of the Museum of Oxford. The exhibits were finally selected and this catalogue prepared in the Department of Western Manuscripts. The catalogue was seen through the press by Miss Grace Briggs and Mrs Joanna Dodsworth.

The following have kindly agreed to allow materials from their collections to be included: the Principal and Fellows of Brasenose College; the Dean and Canons of Christ Church; the Rector and Fellows of Exeter College; the Warden and Fellows of New College; the Visitors of the Ashmolean Museum; the Keeper of the University Archives; the Oxford City Council; the Department of Museums Services, Oxfordshire County Council; the Oxfordshire County Record Office; the Oxfordshire County Libraries; the Editor of the History of Oxford University; the Oxford Preservation Trust; Barclays Bank Limited; Benfield and Loxley Limited; Morrells Brewery Limited; Walters and Co. (Oxford) Limited; Frank Pickstock, Esq.

The exhibition would not have been mounted at all, nor the catalogue published, without generous financial help from a number of firms and other authorities within the city, and from colleges and departments within the university. A full list is given opposite and additional notes on p. 64. This in itself is a notable example of cooperation between town and gown. The Bodleian Library is immensely grateful to them all.   D. G. VAISEY   *Keeper of Western Manuscripts*

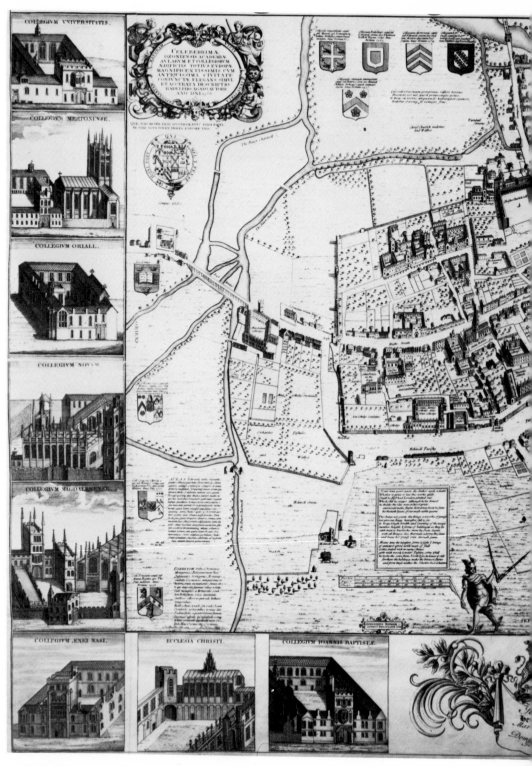

5 Oxford in 1578, drawn by Ralph Agas.

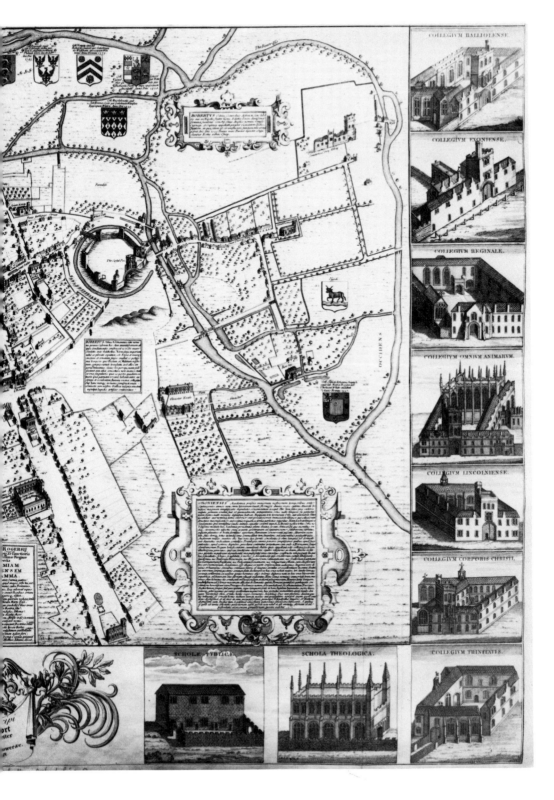

COLLEGIVM BALLIOLENSE.

COLLEGIVM EXONIENSE.

COLLEGIVM REGINALE.

COLLEGIVM OMNIVM ANIMARVM.

COLLEGIVM LINCOLNIENSE.

COLLEGIVM CORPORIS CHRISTI.

SCHOLÆ PVBLICÆ.

SCHOLA THEOLOGICA.

COLLEGIVM TRINITATIS.

Catalogue of the exhibits

At the end of each entry is a note of ownership of the item(s) described. In the case of items from the Bodleian and the University Archives complete shelfmarks are supplied. This has also been done with some other items where relevant. Abbreviations used are:

Ashm. = Ashmolean Museum
Bodl. = Bodleian Library
OCA = Oxford City Archives
OCL = Oxfordshire County Libraries

OCM = Oxfordshire County Council,
Museums Services
OCRO = Oxfordshire County Record Office
OUA = Oxford University Archives

4   The Golden Cross Inn: drawing by John Buckler, 1824.

1 TOPOGRAPHY

The town and the physical growth of the university and colleges within it

Oxford was an important town in the late Anglo-Saxon and early medieval period before the university came into existence. It was surrounded by walls and dominated by the castle to the west. By the mid-thirteenth century a growing prosperity had led to an expansion outside the walls into, for instance, the suburbs of St. Thomas and St. Giles.

For a variety of reasons this prosperity did not survive the later Middle Ages. Economic decline set in, which not only facilitated the establishment and expansion of the university in an area where land was cheap, but led to the virtual dependence of the city on the university, a dependence which lasted until the coming of the motor industry in the twentieth century. These economic changes were reflected in the late medieval buildings: as town buildings decayed, new university buildings appeared, so that, to take one notable example, a derelict strip of land which had become the haunt of undesirable characters provided the site for William of Wykeham's grand new educational establishment of New College in 1379.

The sixteenth and seventeenth centuries saw an improvement in the fortunes of both city and university, despite the disruption caused by the Reformation and the Civil War. Within the walls, and outside them, open land was built on and great new structures appeared. Eight colleges were founded and constructed. The Schools quadrangle of the Bodleian (1613–19) and the Sheldonian Theatre (1663–9), built where streets had formerly been, were the forerunners of a massive rebuilding of the whole area between St. Mary's Church and Broad Street. Later, in the eighteenth century, not only were colleges providing themselves with handsome new buildings to suit a new kind of wealthy student (Queen's College and All Souls College are particularly grand examples), but much new development was taking place in the city. New frontages on shops, the new Covered Market, the Radcliffe Infirmary, the new road to the west, all date from this period.

The nineteenth century again saw the size of Oxford's population increase, with an expansion in the number of inhabitants of the city in the early part of the century, and in the number of university members in the later part. This led to a great increase in the number of houses built and the virtual creation of the densely populated areas of St. Ebbe's, Jericho, St. Clement's and, later, the North Oxford suburb. This development was greatly aided by improved transport facilities, notably the railway, which enabled both people and building materials to be moved easily into the area. The university began its expansion northwards with the construction of the University Museum as the first building in what was to become the Science Area, while alongside it appeared Keble College, a new foundation in startling red brick to provide an Oxford education for the less well-off. At the same time, as the university expanded its numbers, it became more closely integrated with the town through the lodging-house system which grew up after 1868. The town, too, as it changed in shape, acquired a new-found sense of purpose and civic pride, symbolized most vividly, following the acquisition of county borough status in 1889, by the construction of the magnificent new Town Hall in St. Aldate's.

The arrival of the motor-car industry in the twentieth century gave to the city a new economic independence and led to another great expansion on its eastern flank. This expansion has been accompanied, at least until the 1980s, by a steady growth in the university marked by the provision of women's colleges, the development of the science area, the growth in the Bodleian's buildings, and the foundation of new colleges primarily to house the rapidly expanding numbers of postgraduate researchers.

The maps in this section illustrate these centuries of development. The photographs and plans show how some of the grand eighteenth-, nineteenth-, and twentieth-century buildings altered the face of Oxford.

I

Medieval Oxford

This map of Oxford has been compiled by Julian Munby to show the town as it had developed by about 1400. It shows clearly how the castle (see no. 25) was built to dominate the walled town from its western edge. The town's basic street plan, centred on the Carfax crossing, was already clear. This still survives, though many of the small parishes, each with its own church, have now disappeared. Religious houses, such as St. Frideswide's and the Hospital of St. John, were prominent. Students learnt from their masters for the most part in Academic Halls, many not much bigger than normal domestic quarters. These were scattered all round the town. The great college buildings designed to house and support dons and students, and grouped around an inward-facing quadrangle, did not then dominate the town centre. The first of them — New College — had only just been built.

Map drawn for the History of Oxford University

2

An academic hall

In 1438 Tackley's Inn on the High Street was divided into two and the western part was leased to a Master Richard Bulkeley or Buckley. It became known as Buckley Hall and was typical of the academic halls scattered throughout the centre of Oxford, though Buckley himself taught not undergraduates but schoolboys. This is an example of a building which over the centuries has gone from academic to commercial use. It now houses the main Oxford branch of the Abbey National Building

Society. The western elevation drawn by James Green in about 1750 is still easily recognizable. The roof timbers date from the early sixteenth century.

Bodl. MS.Gough Oxon.50, fol.18

3

St. Edmund Hall

A plate from David Loggan's *Oxonia illustrata* of 1675 shows St. Edmund Hall in the later seventeenth century. Though it is to this day called hall it has since 1957 been a college. It can claim, however, to be the only teaching hall still surviving from the Middle Ages. The hall, though not these buildings, is shown on the map in no. 1 above. The range in Loggan's engraving fronts on to Queen's Lane and was constructed in the first half of the seventeenth century. St. Edmund Hall has expanded to the east, north, and south of these buildings, and has in recent years converted the redundant city church of St. Peter in the East (the pedimented gate to which can be seen in this engraving) as its library.

Bodl. MS.Top.Oxon.c.19, no.114

4

A medieval inn

One of two remaining medieval inns in Oxford is the Golden Cross in Cornmarket. The other is the Mitre. The Golden Cross can trace its origins back to the reign of Henry II and was known in its early days as Maugershall or Mauger's Inn. It has been known as the Cross Inn since at least the fourteenth century;

the adjective 'Golden' was not added until the nineteenth century. John Buckler made this drawing of the inn in 1824, a year before it was sold by New College to a group of city businessmen. It illustrates the quadrangular layout, common to many inns but which survives in Oxford only at the Golden Cross. The drawing shows architecture primarily of a seventeenth-century date but this overlies an earlier structure. The importance of town inns as both commercial and artistic centres in earlier centuries is well known, and there is documentary evidence of visiting groups of actors performing in this courtyard in the seventeenth century. A strong tradition holds that Shakespeare's company, and indeed Shakespeare himself, visited these premises.

Bodl. MS.Don.a.2(26)

5

Oxford in 1578

This map (which is aligned with south at the top) was made by Ralph Agas in 1578. The main difference between the picture that it gives and that given by the map of 1400 lies in the large amount of open space which had appeared within the city. Oxford's wealth and importance declined in the later Middle Ages, leading to a contraction of the built-up area and the decay of many buildings. Some of the space thus created was acquired by the colleges but much remained derelict for long periods.

The city walls were still very much in evidence and a number of buildings survived on the site of the castle, although many of them were ruinous. The religious houses, and the colleges for their members, had been dissolved, but some of their sites had been taken over by secular colleges: St. John's Hospital by Magdalen College, for example, St. Frideswide's Priory by Christ Church, and Durham College by Trinity. The Divinity School stood north of St. Mary's Church as the only building owned by the university. Above it the empty room which had held Duke Humfrey's library awaited the arrival of Sir Thomas Bodley to revitalize it. All but eight of the academic halls had gone. They had been replaced by colleges, and Agas's map shows how the quadrangular plan selected by William of Wykeham for New College in the 1370s had become the norm, even though some, such as Christ Church, had not yet closed the square. Almost all these college buildings can be seen to be

occupying the higher, dry, ground to the east of the city's north–south axis.

Bodl. Gough Maps Oxon.1

6

Oxford in 1750

By the time that Isaac Taylor surveyed Oxford in 1750 the boundaries of the town portrayed by Agas had been blurred by much building. Taylor's map showed four derelict areas. Though some of the old city wall remained, it had no defensive purpose, and the city had spread outside it and made busy streets of, for example, Holywell, St. Giles, and George Street. Much new building had been undertaken in the areas behind the main street frontages. The heavier shading denoting college and university buildings picks out the great new eighteenth-century edifices both in the area north of St. Mary's Church and, for example, at Magdalen College. The Radcliffe Camera had been opened in the year before this survey was undertaken. Nevertheless Oxford still retained many of the hallmarks of a medieval town. There was no proper road out to the west, the city was still gated to the east and north, and the butchers' shops remained in the centre of what is now Queen Street.

Bodl. Gough Maps Oxon.13

7

Oxford in 1900

The Ordnance Survey map of Oxford revised in 1898 shows the large increase in building since 1750. The need for more housing had led to development on all sides of the city, but particularly noticeable is the spread northwards including the areas round Beaumont Street, Wellington Square, and Jericho. The growth and modernization of the university is symbolized by the beginnings of the Science Area based on the University Museum (1855–60) and the Examination Schools (1876–82) in the High Street. Keble College (1868–82) had been built, while new denominational colleges such as Mansfield (1886) and Manchester (1889) had transferred to Oxford from other areas.

By this date the city had cast off the medieval trappings which had still been evident in 1750. Tramways ran down the new road to the west where one of the railway stations is visible, three churches (St. Peter le Bailey, St. Martin at Carfax, and St. Clement) had been pulled down to allow for street improvements; and the new Town Hall, opened in 1897, symbolized the city's new confidence as a county borough.

OCRO O.S. 2nd ed. (1900), Oxon.XXXIII.15

8–9

Radcliffe Square and the Camera

The area now known as Radcliffe Square, with the Camera as its focus, represents all that emerged from the ambitious scheme by the architect Nicholas Hawksmoor to redesign the whole of this part of Oxford. As a copy of a plan drawn in the 1730s shows, whole courts and rows of tenements stretching right up to the south wall of the Schools quadrangle were swept away in order to create an open space to contain the vast circular building. Originally, however, the construction of a library with money bequeathed in 1714 by Dr John Radcliffe, physician to Queen Anne, was simply one part of the great replanning of what had become the university's geographical centre. A plan, probably made by Hawksmoor himself at the time of Radcliffe's death, shows that his scheme was to make the square a *Forum Universitatis* with a statue of Queen Anne at its centre. This was to be balanced by a *Forum Civitatis* at Carfax. North of what was then All Souls garden (now the Codrington Library) was to be a new university church (*Capella Universitatis*), and north of that an open space (*Pomoerium*) was to replace the 'sheds and scandalous houses' and provide a vista down to New College. To the west of the Sheldonian Theatre a new laboratory (*Elaboratorium*) was to jut out into Broad Street, while a house for the university printer (*Domus Architypografi*) was to stand in Exeter College garden. When this plan was made, two sites for a circular Radcliffe Library were being considered: one, outlined in pencil, on the west end of the Bodleian, and the other attached to the south wall of the Schools quadrangle. For a variety of reasons, mostly aesthetic, a site in the centre of the new square was chosen for the library and the rest of Hawksmoor's plan came to naught. The Camera was eventually built to the designs not of Hawksmoor but of James Gibbs.

Bodl. MS.Top.gen.b.64, fol.459
Bodl. MS.Top.Oxon.a.26(R)

The Indian Institute corner

The corner of Catte Street and Holywell in the late nineteenth century underwent a transformation similar to that which Radcliffe Square had experienced in the eighteenth. Commercial premises and private dwellings had occupied the site, and the main building on the corner had been from at least 1754 a coffee-house, known as Bagg's coffee-house in the eighteenth century and Seal's in the nineteenth. It was a distinguished building and has been attributed to Sir John Vanbrugh, the architect of Blenheim Palace.

The Indian Institute building was erected in two building operations between 1883 and 1896, and photographs survive which show the corner immediately before construction work began and after the completion of the first part of the building in 1884. The eighteenth-century lines of the coffee-house gave way to a mixture of Gothic and Oriental designed by Basil Champneys, and a group of shops and houses disappeared in the creation of a university teaching institute. The Institute was intended as a centre for instruction and research on all subjects relative to India, and fulfilled that function until 1960, though the training of candidates for the Indian Civil Service had ceased in 1940. The building is now the Modern History Faculty centre and library.

OCL Photos 835 and 4260

12–13

The University Museum and the Parks

If some developments by the university led to a depletion of amenities for the city, others certainly led to their enlargement. Nowhere is this more evident than in the University Parks and in the museums which the university created and maintains. A pen-and-ink drawing by Joseph Fisher in about 1835 shows how rural the area north of Wadham College was at that date. It had changed little in the time since Isaac Taylor's map (no. 6) was drawn, and where the University Museum and its surrounding laboratories now stand were then two fields owned by Merton College. These formed the Parks, and their allocation as a site for the new

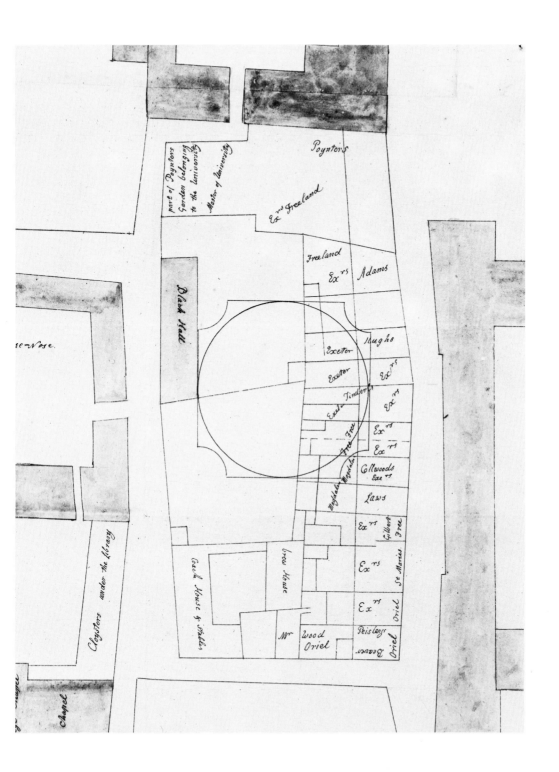

8   Area designated for Radcliffe Camera, showing existing tenements, *c.* 1730.

museum provoked controversy. The present Parks, which were greatly extended under university ownership from 1854 onwards, have since that time provided an open space for general public use while providing playing fields for university and college clubs.

One of the objections to siting the Museum in the Parks was that it would be too far out from the main geographical centre of the university; but its construction on this open site did not entail any destruction of commercial or domestic buildings. A contemporary engraving shows the building nearing completion in 1860. It was the result of sustained pressure by Dr (later Sir) Henry Acland for a centre for scientific study in Oxford, and was a triumph for the architectural views of John Ruskin. The eventual design by Benjamin Woodward stands as an extraordinary product of the Gothic Revival. The laboratory building on the right was modelled on the abbot's kitchen at Glastonbury Abbey in Somerset. Not only did this development signal the arrival of modern scientific study at the university, but it provided a natural history museum for university and city, to stand alongside the museum of the humanities at the Ashmolean which had been built between 1841 and 1845.

Bodl. MS.Top.Oxon.b.89, fol.52
Bodl. G.A.Oxon.a.47, no.53

14–17

Broad Street and the New Bodleian

One of the sites considered for the construction of the University Museum in the 1850s was the corner of Broad Street and Parks Road where, incidentally, Dr Henry Acland himself lived. The buildings on that site, themselves the product of the expansion of the city outside its walls in the seventeenth and eighteenth centuries, were reprieved then but were subsequently to be swept away to make way for the New Bodleian Library in the 1930s. The commercial premises, private dwellings, public houses, and other institutions occupying that corner were replaced by the enormous steel and concrete structure faced with squared rubble designed by Sir Giles Gilbert Scott and completed in 1940. The ceremonial of the official opening by King George VI on 24 October 1946 was considerably enlivened when the silver key broke in the lock. Scott's design for the new library was not the only one produced in the 1930s. Another by A. S. G. Butler would have given the corner an even more distinctive appearance.

Bodl. MS.Top.Oxon.a.77 (two photos)
Bodl. Official opening programme
Bodl. Broken key

18   Extract from the Anglo-Saxon Chronicle relating to Oxford in 911.

2 HISTORY

The origins and early development of city and university

Neither the city nor the university can trace its beginnings to an exact date and each has attracted its fair share of myth in consequence. According to one account the town was founded in the time of the prophet Samuel by a certain King Mempric (whose only good act it was), and in another the university had its origins in a school established by Greek philosophers who came to Britain after the fall of Troy.

Oxford in fact owes its name and perhaps its origin to its position at a major crossing point of the Thames — a ford suitable for oxen. From very early times the site lay near an important north–south route, and archaeological excavations have revealed evidence of intermittent occupation from the Mesolithic period onwards. Although the first mention of Oxford in recorded history does not occur until 911, it is likely that there was already a settlement there in the eighth century associated with a monastic foundation. The town grew in prominence during the later Anglo-Saxon period. It was incorporated into the West Saxon system of fortified burhs for defence against the Danes, and like other burhs it was probably a market town from this date. Lying on an important trade route, Oxford rapidly flourished. By 1066 it had expanded well beyond its original walls and with over a thousand houses was the sixth largest town in England. It continued to prosper in the twelfth and early thirteenth centuries as a result of its trade in cloth and wool.

The university began to make its appearance in the twelfth century. A succession of individuals teaching in the town developed gradually into a loose association of masters and scholars, emerging in the next century as a more organized society which rapidly began to play an important part in the development of the town. Protected and encouraged by successive kings, the university began to acquire considerable power over the day-to-day running of the town, and the presence of a large body of scholars was bound to have a significant effect on its economy. By the early thirteenth century both town and gown were well established.

18

The origins of the town

'This year died Ethelred, Ealdorman of the Mercians, and King Edward took possession of London and Oxford and all the lands belonging to them.' The Anglo-Saxon Chronicle under the year 911 contains this earliest recorded reference to Oxford. It follows that Oxford was already an important place by this date, and may have had its origins in a lay settlement which grew up outside the gates of an eighth-century monastery. The tradition, recounted by the twelfth-century chronicler William of Malmesbury, is that Frideswide, a king's daughter, having vowed to become a nun, fled to Oxford to escape a suitor. When he tried to enter the town in pursuit he was struck blind, but regained his sight at her prayer. Frideswide then founded a monastery at Oxford, where she eventually died.

William presumably derived his information from St. Frideswide's Priory, which was founded in 1122 and may have preserved the tradition of an older house whose site, endowments, and dedication it had acquired. The story must be largely imaginary but behind the legend may lie a basis of fact.

Bodl. MS.Laud Misc.636, fol.35

19

Early coins minted at Oxford

Oxford's early importance is reflected in coinage. Coins with the mint name 'Orsnaforda' or 'Ohsnaforda' and bearing the name of King Alfred have been attributed to an Oxford mint. Surviving coins are mostly probably Viking imitations, but it is possible that they were copied from a genuine coin of Alfred minted at Oxford. Certainly the town's importance during the reign of Athelstan (924–39) is indicated by its possession of four moneyers, a higher number than any other borough save London and Winchester, and there are known moneyers in Oxford throughout the tenth century. The sack of Oxford by the Danes in 1009 seems to have put the mint out of action for a time, but it survived as a minting place until the closure of provincial mints in 1250.

Ashm.

20

Oxford in Domesday

By 1066 Oxford was undoubtedly one of England's major towns. The description of the town in the Domesday Book lists 1,018 houses inside and outside the walls at that date. It certainly possessed six parish churches by this time and may have had as many as ten. Only London, York, Norwich, Lincoln and Winchester exceeded it in size. But by 1086 the town had suffered a severe set-back; 583 houses are recorded as 'waste' at that date, and although some were presumably destroyed by the building of the castle in 1071, this could not account for all of them. The reasons for its decline are unknown; it may be due to an unrecorded disaster such as a fire or flood, or to the general falling-off in trade which followed the Conquest. This set-back, however, was only temporary. The

twelfth and early thirteenth centuries saw intensive building activity, based on a rising prosperity from increased trade and the expansion of the university.

Facsimile of Oxfordshire entry in Domesday Book

21

The 1191 charter

The 1191 charter is a confirmation of a grant of the island of Medley to Osney Abbey in 1147 by 'the citizens of Oxford of the commune of the city and of the merchant guild'. It shows that by this date the citizens were able to act alone as a corporate body. The 1147 grant had required an intermediary, William de Chesney, constable of Oxford Castle and alderman of the guild, to declare that the city had granted the island to him and consented to its further grant to Osney. By 1191 the abbey found a charter executed by the citizens alone sufficient security. The town's common seal attached to this deed is the earliest known municipal seal in Great Britain. It depicts a walled city with an ox superimposed; inside the walls are three cylindrical towers. This seal remained in use until 1662 when the council decided that 'by reason of its absurd, ill and unhandsome cutting' it was 'dishonourable to the Cittie and unfit to be used'.

OCA

22

Charter of privileges, 1199

In 1199 King John granted the borough to the burgesses to hold at a higher farm than that paid in the time of Henry II and Richard, and also confirmed their privileges generally. A grant of fee farm set the royal dues at a fixed annual sum and authorized the townsmen to collect it through their own officials without the intervention of the sheriff. In effect it recognized the existence of a corporate body which could be held responsible for its dues to the king. The privileges confirmed were those of the town's first known charter, granted by Henry II in about 1155, which itself confirmed liberties enjoyed under Henry I. These included all the customs, liberties and laws of London, and trading rights with the capital. Oxford's liberties became the model for those of several other towns.

OCA H.27.1

20 Oxford as recorded in the Domesday Book.

Sciant presentes et futuri quod nos Cives Oxenefordie de communi Civitatis et de Gilda mer-
catoria pro salute nostra ac nostrorum et animabus parentum et antecessorum nostrorum concedimus et presenti carta nostra confir-
mamus Ecclesie sancte Marie de Osenea et Canonicis in ea deo servientibus Donationem quam antecessores
nostri eis fecerunt de Insula de Middeneia cum omnibus pertinenciis ei Ita ut singulis annis ad festum sancti
Michaelis reddant ipsi Canonici dimidiam marcam argenti pro hac eadem tenatia ubi nos iusserimus
sicut testatur Cirographium antecessorum nostrorum quod eis de donatione eiusdem Insule fecerunt. Preterea
quia nos cepimus in manu pro nobis et pro heredibus nostris warantandi predictam Insulam eisdem Canonicis ubique et versus omnes homines ipsi pro hac warantatione solvent nobis et heredibus nostris singulis annis ad
Pascha aliam dimidiam marcam quam tradent eu nos iusserimus. Et nos et heredes nostri fideliter waran-
tabimus eis idem tenementum pro servitio predicte marce annue pro omnibus rebus et pro omnibus servitiis. Hanc
nostram concessionem et confirmationem fecimus nos communi consilio Civitatis et communali sigillo nostro confir-
mamus. Hii sunt autem qui hanc concessionem et confirmationem fecerunt. Hugellus te Decan' Orenef'.
Johs kepeherm et henr' fil' Segrim: te aldermanni. Laur' kepehm et Thom de Thademar
cona: te pretores. Petr' fil' Gaufridi. Will's fil' pretoris. Will' fil' Rad'. Thom fil' Ailrici. hen-
ric' fil' Simeonis. Laur' fil' hardingi. Rad' padi. Wale' fil' Giel. Will' fil' knihr. Segar mer-
cator. Rog' fil' Sewer. Johs fil' Ailnod. Walger' vinitari'. Adam rufus. Barthol' Grosmarchie.
Rog' fil' Burewold. Gileb' fil' Buroldi. Jocelino fil' Safari. Rad' Coleman. Will' fil' Rog' filii Si-
wardi et hug' fr' ei'. Aluredus delmelena. Owein et Rob' fili'ei'. Benet fil' Ailnod. Rad' fil' Bur'.
henr' de Chaudre. et Lambin' frat' ei'. Will' pileu. Wale' pille. Will' fil' Amfridi fil' pretoris.
Rad' Cordewanari' fili' Simonis Cordewan'. henr' de Lisewis. hug' aurifab'. Ric' fr' ei'. Petr'
fil' Johis. Johs aurifab'. Nichol' fil' Sewer. Wale' halgod. et Rad' fr' ei'. Rad' kepehm et Benet
frat' ei'. Adam vinitari'. Johs fili' henr' diei. Nichol' fil' Will' fil' Rad'. henr' fil' Gaufr' fil'
Bodim et Ric' fr' ei'. Will' husari' de Osen. et hug' fili' ei'. henr' diei' te clicus prety. Ric' fili'
hardingi. Rob' fil' wimare. Benedict' fil' paulini. Rob' fil' Gaufr' fil' Bodini medarii. Thom
fil' Cadwun. et henr' fr' ei'. Rog' fil' fulconis. Et totum commune einu Civitatis Oxenefordi;

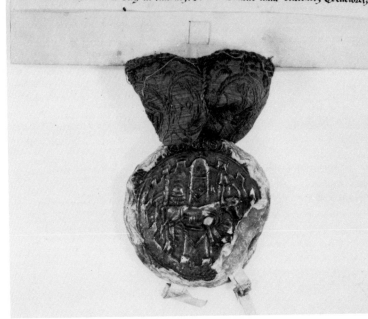

21   Charter of 1191 granting Medley Island to Osney Abbey.

23
A royal visit

Matthew Paris's *Chronica Maiora* refers to the visit of King John to Oxford in 1205 when he spent Christmas in the town. This was just one of many visits made to the town by English kings. Oxford seems to have possessed a royal residence in the tenth century. Several important councils were held in the town in the half-century before the Conquest, and although the Norman kings visited Oxford infrequently, royal interest revived with the building of the king's house, later known as Beaumont Palace, outside the north gate in the early twelfth century. Oxford played a prominent role in the civil war of Stephen's reign; Henry II made several visits to Oxford, four councils were held there during his reign, and his sons, Richard and John, were born there. John himself visited the town frequently and during the troubles of 1215 the town was chosen several times as a meeting place for the opposing parties.

Bodl. MS.Douce 207, fol.154

24
The city wall

The first town wall was probably built in the late ninth or early tenth century when Oxford formed part of the West Saxon system of burhs, built for defence against the Danes. This Saxon wall was built of turves with a stone revetment. The fortifications were extended and improved in succeeding centuries, and between 1226 and 1240 the walls were thoroughly overhauled and the remaining sections of rampart replaced by stone. Despite occasional attempts at repair, however, the wall had largely fallen into decay by the sixteenth century. As Taylor's map of 1750 (no. 6) shows, most of it had disappeared by that date. The photograph shows part of the surviving section of the thirteenth-century wall in the grounds of New College during the course of an inspection by the city authorities in May 1962. The grant of the land on which the wall stood was made to the college's founder, William of Wykeham, in 1379 on condition that the college kept the wall in good repair and allowed the mayor to inspect it every three years. This obligation has been observed up to the present, and every third year the mayor, sheriff, aldermen and councillors march in procession to carry out their inspection.

Bodl. G.A.Oxon.b.200, no.11

25
The castle

Oxford Castle was built for the king by Robert D'Oilly in 1071 and played a part in the military affairs of the kingdom in the Middle Ages. It was besieged by King Stephen during the civil war in 1142, and it was then that Queen Matilda made her well-known escape from the castle across the snow. It fell under siege again in 1216, this time by the forces of the barons. It was improved and maintained throughout this period but thereafter gradually fell into disuse and was said to be ruinous in 1388. Nevertheless it was the headquarters successively of both royalist and parliamentary garrisons during the Civil War. The castle was owned by the Crown until 1611 but shortly afterwards passed to Christ Church. The plan displayed was drawn up about 1617 soon after its purchase. The college held it until 1785 when it was sold to enlarge the gaol. The site was settled in trust on the inhabitants of Oxfordshire in 1850.

Christ Church Maps, Oxford St. George 1

26
St. George's in the castle

A photograph of the crypt, which, together with the tower, is all that survives of the church of St. George in the castle. The collegiate church of St. George is said to have been founded in 1074 by Robert D'Oilly, but there may well have been a pre-Conquest church on the site. Its position and status as a parish church from an early date support this. It was superseded as a parish church by St. Thomas's in the thirteenth century, but continued to serve the inhabitants of the castle and the surrounding area until the late sixteenth century. The crypt itself was largely destroyed in 1794 but the surviving portions were re-erected in a new cellar and enlarged in the mid-nineteenth century following the discovery of more original stonework.

Bodl. Dep.a.25, fol.92

27
The mythical origins of the university

A copy of the university statutes written in 1477 includes the *Historiola* or mythical account of the

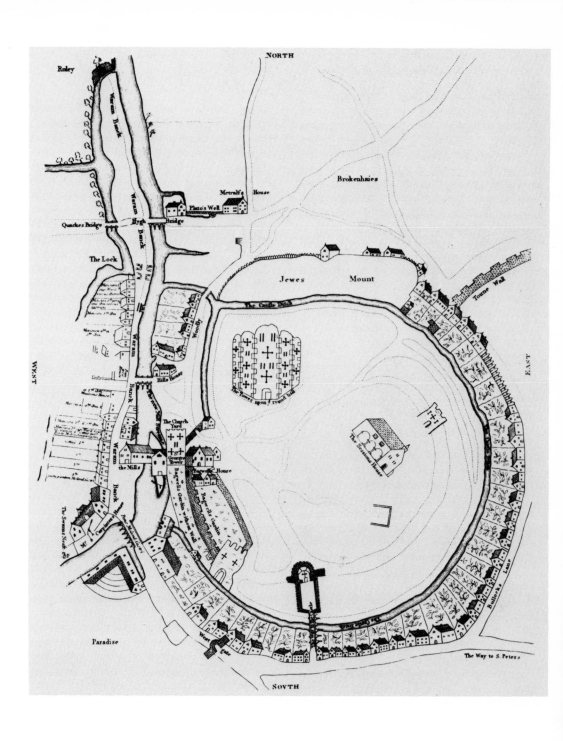

25   Plan of Oxford Castle, *c.* 1617.

origins of Oxford university. It traces them to a school established at 'Grekelade' (Cricklade) by Greek philosophers who had accompanied the Trojan Brutus to Britain after the fall of Troy. The school is later said to have moved to Oxford because of the pleasantness of its position, 'in antiquity formerly named Bellositum'. The story is an unlikely one, to say the least, and it is generally agreed that the university had no one founder, but developed gradually in the twelfth century through the activities of individual scholars. The religious houses in the neighbourhood of Oxford and their concern with learning provided the environment for this activity: the college of secular canons of St. George's in the castle (no. 26) may have been the earliest to encourage it.

OUA NEP supra, Reg.B, fol.1ᵛ

28–9

Early scholars at Oxford

References to Oxford studies in the twelfth century are few and largely unconnected. Here and there individual teachers are mentioned, the earliest being Theobaldus Stampensis (Thibaut d'Estampes), a Norman secular priest who is described as 'magister Oxinefordie'. He is stated to have lectured on secular literature to audiences of clerks at Oxford ranging in number from sixty to a hundred. Theobaldus was probably teaching between 1116 and 1120 and perhaps both before and after these dates. This manuscript, which dates from the second half of the twelfth century, contains a diatribe against monks addressed by him to

27 Mythical account of the university's origins: passage in statutes of 1477.

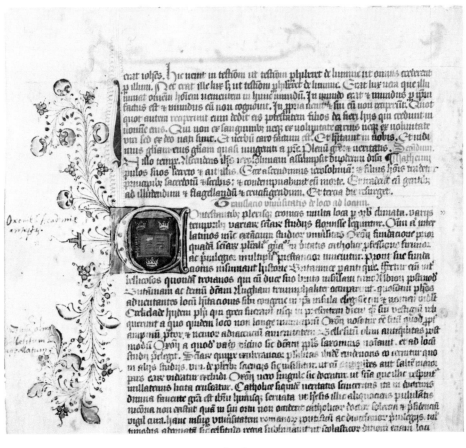

30   University's charter of privileges, 1214.

Thurstan, Archbishop of York. The other manuscript displayed is a mid-fourteenth-century copy of the *Cronica de adventu Normannorum in Angliam,* which covers the years 1066–1269. In 1133 Robert Pullen is said to have lectured on the bible at Oxford and preached every Lord's Day to the people. There are other isolated references to individual scholars elsewhere, but the best evidence for a flourishing school at Oxford in the twelfth century comes from Giraldus Cambrensis, who around 1187 says he visited the town and spent three days there reading one of his works to the doctors and scholars of the various faculties and to the townspeople.

Bodl. MS. Bodley 561, fol.61
Bodl. MS. Bodley 712, fol.275ᵃ

30

The university's charter of privileges

In 1209 two Oxford clerks were hanged by the townsmen in revenge for the alleged murder of a woman. Feeling they were unlikely to receive support from King John when the country lay under an interdict, the scholars dispersed. When the king made his peace with the pope in 1213 the town likewise submitted to papal authority. On 25 June 1214 the pope's legate, Nicholas of Tusculum, issued the ordinance shown. It contains a recital of the financial penalties inflicted on the town and also the privileges granted to scholars. Among other things it commanded the town to feast one hundred poor scholars annually and to sell food and other necessities to scholars at reasonable prices. The chief privilege gained by the university was that the town had to hand over any arrested clerk to the ecclesiastical authority, the first step towards the independence of the university from the town. The document also called for the appointment of a chancellor of the university, the first reference to such an official. As a result the university emerged as a stronger, more organized body.

OUA WPβ/P/12/1

31

Catte Street, c.1215

By this deed Helyas Bradfodt granted land in Catte Street in the parish of St. Mary the Virgin to William son of Robert of Northampton. Its significance lies in the list of witnesses to the transaction at the end. It includes several individuals whose occupations associate them with the university — 'scriptor' (scribe), 'ligator' (bookbinder), 'illuminator', 'parcamenerius' (parchment-maker). A date as early as 1180 has been assigned to this deed which would increase its importance as evidence for the existence of an organized body of scholars requiring men with such skills, but a date a generation later seems more likely.

OUA WPβ/F/46

Town and gown in the later medieval period

The latter part of the thirteenth century was marked by increasing violence between town and gown which continued well into the fourteenth century. This can be attributed to a reversal of their relative positions. For a variety of reasons the town gradually declined in wealth and importance during this period. The most important factor was that changes in the organization of the cloth trade favoured rural areas. Oxford ceased to figure in any important way in national politics and became a county and market town of purely local significance. At the same time the university was expanding, and successive settlements and agreements with the town tended to increase its powers at the townsmen's expense, while the town's economy became more and more dependent on supplying the university's needs. The continuing reduction of Oxford's trade and population also allowed the colleges to acquire central sites for building and still further reduced the commercial area. All these factors contributed to a growing social unrest which culminated in the great town and gown riot on St. Scholastica's day in 1355. Though the town won that battle the university might be said to have won the war. The settlement which followed so increased the university's privileges that henceforth it controlled many aspects of town life. This ascendancy may in fact have led to the improved relations between the two bodies during the latter part of the medieval period. Disputes continued, but the physical violence which had characterized the earlier ones was missing and there is evidence of both sides working in harmony.

32

Privileges

The award in 1214 (no. 30) is the first extant charter granting privileges to the university. That charter was granted by a papal legate, but it was followed during the thirteenth and the first half of the fourteenth centuries by a number of royal grants of privileges to the university. The crown wished to protect and encourage the university which provided a supply of learned men for administrative and clerical purposes, and with every grant its position in relation to the town was strengthened. However, the town was a well-established borough before the university developed in its midst and it had privileges of its own on which the university was apt to encroach. Further,

the scholars as consumers were economically heavily dependent on the townsmen who were the producers. It was inevitable, therefore, that there would be clashes between the two bodies when the privileges of each would be called in question by the other. This happened frequently in the thirteenth and fourteenth centuries. The letters patent of King Edward I shown here and dated 18 May 1287 appointed justices to inquire into one such alleged infringement of university privileges by the town.

OUA WPβ/M/2

33–4

A town and university riot

On Friday 21 February 1297/8 a riot broke out in Oxford which lasted for four days. As might be

44 Drawings by J. Bereblock of new buildings of the fourteenth–fifteenth centuries.

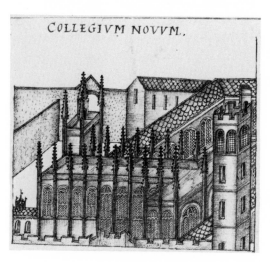

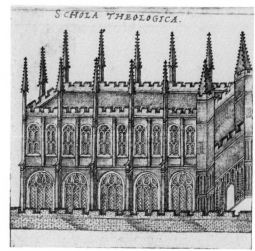

expected, the truth about how the trouble started is not easy to discover since different accounts of it, some written by citizens and some by scholars, survive. The results of the riot are clear enough: there was a good deal of damage and two people died, Thomas Attechircheye of the city and Fulco de Neyrmit of the university. On 27 February the king, Edward I, in the deed shown here, appointed two justices, William de Bereford and Henry de This-telden, to hold an inquiry and to proceed to a settlement. The accompanying roll records, in French, the city's version of what happened, saying that on Monday in the feast of St. Matthew (24 February) a force of over three thousand clerks (*treis mil e plus des clers de la universite*) conducted a planned assault on the town. This was doubtless an exaggeration, as was the university's account that on that day a few clerks were attacked by the whole commune of the town in full battle cry. The final adjudication left the university with its powers and privileges enhanced.

The roll is an interesting survival from the medieval city records, most of which were lost during the period between 1640 and 1660. The document was certainly in the city archives in 1626 but, at an unknown time probably during the Civil War, it migrated into the archives of the university.

OUA WPβ/M/1
OUA SEP/Y/12

35–8

St. Scholastica's Day riot

The greatest university and city riot of all started on 10 February 1354/5. Once again, two accounts of it survive: one from the university's point of view and another from that of the city. The trouble began in the Swindlestock Tavern where some scholars apparently threw wine in the face of the landlord and then beat him with a quart pot. The town bailiffs tried to restore order but failed, and a riot broke out. The Swindlestock Tavern stood on the south-west corner of Carfax. It was subsequently known as the Mermaid and was pulled down in about 1708 when the street was widened. Candle-sticks and drinking pots, always to hand in a tavern, provided convenient weapons once fighting broke out and were capable of inflicting painful wounds when wielded with force.

The university's version of what happened (no. 37) was given in a submission to the Bishop of Lincoln in whose diocese Oxford then was. It survives in a copy made in the seventeenth century by the first Keeper of the University Archives, Brian Twyne. It glossed over the scene in the Swindle-stock Tavern which would have left the university with the blame for the riot, saying merely that a quarrel had arisen between town and gown. It went

COLLEGIVM MERTONENSE.

COLLEGIVM MAGDALENEN

on to accuse the townsmen of using the occasion to attack the university as if they had been looking for such an opportunity (*quasi ex malitia praecogitata occasionem quaerentes conflictum cum scholaribus habendi*). Many of the scholars who had not been able to take shelter in their colleges had been, it was claimed, driven out of Oxford. The submission ends with a list of those who were killed or mortally injured in the fighting.

The city's version of the events (no. 38) also survives in a copy by Brian Twyne. Like its forerunner in 1297/8 (no. 34) it is in French. It describes the outbreak of the trouble in the Swindlestock Tavern, and emphasizes that after this the scholars armed themselves and attacked the mayor and other townsmen. The riot is then presented as a series of unprovoked attacks by the scholars on the townsmen, many of whom were killed or wounded. The differing versions make clear that, once fighting had begun, each side took the opportunity to settle old scores, and there was much indiscriminate bloodshed.

Bodl. MSS.Twyne V, p.137 and IV, p.76
Ashm. Candlestick
OCM Pot

39

The effects of the riot

As a result of the riot both university and city were required to surrender their privileges to the king and new charters were subsequently granted. In them the town's privileges were further reduced while those of the university were increased. The grant to the university, shown here, gave it control of the market, of the assizes for regulating the price and quality of bread, ale and wine, of the assizes for checking weights and measures, of cleaning and paving the streets, and of the punishment of those who carried arms in the town.

The Bishop of Lincoln imposed an annual penance on the townsmen for their violence. Every year on St. Scholastica's Day the mayor, bailiffs and sixty citizens had to attend a mass at St. Mary's for the souls of the clerks and others slain in the riot, and each had to offer a penny. After the Reformation the mass was replaced by a sermon and litany. The university insisted on the performance of the ceremony until 1825.

OUA WPβ/N/5b

40

The fraternity of St. Thomas

The medieval period was not always one of conflict in Oxford. There are many examples of citizens and scholars acting in concert. The fraternity of St. Thomas is such an example. It was an association which flourished in the second half of the fourteenth century and whose members each paid 3s. 4d. per annum towards the stipend of a chantry chaplain to say mass each day for them. The mass was said in St. Thomas's chapel of the church of St. Mary the Virgin. The list of subscribers in 1484 shows that the fraternity had a membership which included masters of arts, a university bedel and a manciple as well as townsmen and their wives. There is evidence that scholars and townsmen met and prayed together as members of this fraternity until at least 1547.

Bodl. MS.Rolls Oxon.14

41–2

The regulation of labour

In 1357 royal letters patent appointed the chancellor and the mayor to be justices under the statute of labourers. The statute, passed in 1351, was an attempt to regulate prices and wages and to prevent them from rising too high because of the scarcity of labour caused by the Black Death. The justices were to fine those who took or paid excessive wages as well as those who overcharged for the goods which they had made. In Oxford chancellor and mayor sat together uniting the two authorities in the enforcement of this law, though for the session shown here — that for March 1390/1 — the chancellor is not recorded as sitting. The roll which records the judgements at the session also shows how colleges attracted to Oxford from other parts of the country craftsmen who then became involved in the life of the town and settled there. Among those accused of having taken excessive wages were William Brown and John Sampson: both were masons who had come to Oxford to work on the building of New College, and Brown in 1396–7 took charge of the building of its bell-tower. The rest of his working life was spent on the construction of New College.

OUA WPβ/N/18
OUA SEP/Y/15, mem.6

43–4

Labourers at work

As skilled craftsmen, masons could command high pay for their work and were frequently fined for exceeding the statutory wages, though they also did their duty in enforcing the law. Another of the New College masons, Richard Norton, was one of the constables whose task it was to collect the fines levied under the statute of labourers in 1391 even though he himself was accused of taking excessive wages in that year and again in 1392 and 1394. The New College account roll for the year 1396–7 records the money spent on building the bell-tower and part of the college wall, work being done by William Brown and his men. The account records the purchase of stone for the building work from Headington quarry. These local quarries also provided stone for a number of college buildings in the fifteenth century, All Souls, Merton and Magdalen amongst them, and considerable quantities were used in the construction of the Divinity School between about 1420 and 1490. Drawings of all these buildings were made by J. Bereblock to illustrate a volume of poems presented to Queen Elizabeth I on her visit to Oxford in 1566.

New College Archives 9128
Bodl. MS.Bodley 13

45–6

The university and a city trade: the Tailors' Company

One of the trades which formed protective associations in Oxford was that of the tailors. Some form of association probably existed by 1306 but the earliest unambiguous reference to a guild is in 1454. In the middle of the fifteenth century the guild's officers were using the mayor's court to recover debts, but the university claimed an interest because tailors made academic robes. Entries in the university letter-book for 1421–1509 show an agreement made between the university and the Tailors' Company in 1491. Under it the university agreed to restrain any tailors who were not members of the tailors' guild, to fine them, and to share the proceeds with the guild. The tailors in return promised to abide by the university statutes governing the price and cut of academic robes, to choose a regent master approved by the university

as their chaplain, and to pay the proctors 3s. 4d. a year. University regulation of the guild continued in the early sixteenth century and some tailors were admitted to the guild by the chancellor. However, by 1531 the university's control of the tailors had passed to the town. In the seventeenth century the university claimed that the company issued restrictive by-laws and charged too much for membership in order to reduce competition.

The company was dissolved in 1838 and its assets were shared among the surviving members. The steward of the company at the time, George P. Hester, was presented with what he called 'the ancient oath book of the Company of Tailors'. This volume, on which the masters of the company took their oaths, might be expected to have been a bible or at least the four gospels. In fact it is a little fifteenth-century hodge-podge of verses from the gospels with a kalendar taken from another manuscript and with many blank leaves. It is an interesting example of a kind of 'magic book' which, regardless of its contents, conferred power and solemnity on an oath.

OUA NEP supra, Reg.F, fol.170ᵛ
Bodl. MS.Morrell 25, fols.16ᵛ–17

47

Academic dress in the fifteenth century

Two illustrations from a fifteenth-century manuscript concerning William of Wykeham by Thomas Chaundler (1418–90) show the sort of academic robes which the tailors of Oxford were accustomed to make. The picture on the left shows Wykeham's foundation of New College viewed from the south and still instantly recognizable. Arranged at the front of the picture are the Warden (Chaundler was Warden from 1453 to 1475) together with most of the seventy fellows or scholars, ten priests or chaplains, and sixteen choristers for which it was founded. All are clothed according to their status or degree. Chaundler also appears in the opposite picture as Thomas *Cancellarius Wellen.* (Chancellor of Wells) on the bottom left. In the centre at the top is the mitred figure of William of Wykeham with New College chapel and hall in his right hand, while to his right stands Archbishop Chichele holding in his hand the chapel of his own foundation, All Souls College.

MS. New College 288, fols.3ᵛ–4

47   Academic dress: the Warden, fellows and other members of New College in the fifteenth century.

47 The founders of New College and All Souls College with other
churchmen, from a fifteenth-century manuscript.

Conflict and cooperation from the sixteenth to the eighteenth centuries

In the later sixteenth century the town began to recover from the long decline of the later Middle Ages. It grew in population and prosperity once more, helped by the revival of the university in Elizabeth's reign after a period of stagnation. The process continued in the seventeenth century and found its physical form in the expansion of the town and the fine university buildings of the period. But this new-found prosperity only served to reawaken the differences between the two bodies over their shared government of the city. Conflict was renewed over a range of issues even wider than previously. Battles were less physical, but no less intense, although the gains on either side hardly justified the effort and money that went into them. The Civil War and Commonwealth scarcely interrupted the struggle (although the period did see some attempt at cooperation), and it was not until the beginning of the eighteenth century, when the university entered a more dormant period and the city's growth had come to an end, that trouble between town and gown subsided once more.

48–9

The great university burglary

In 1544 the university suffered a severe financial blow. The 'horrendum commissum' or 'terrible crime' described in this note prefacing a university account book was the theft of most of its wealth. During the evening of 21 February two men, armed with an iron bar, a hammer, and a pair of pincers, broke open the chests in the university church of St. Mary the Virgin and stole plate and other valuables; they then repeated the performance eleven days later. The thieves, Richard Raunce and John Stanshawe, were quickly detained, tried and sentenced to death. But the university had lost all its cash in hand and had no money for immediate expenses. Fragments of gold and silver plate were collected and put in the charge of Leonard Hutcheson, Master of University College, who sold it off. His acquittance for the sale shows that of the $389\frac{1}{2}$ oz. of scraps collected, he sold 377 oz. for £71.14s.5$\frac{1}{4}$d. The remaining 12$\frac{1}{2}$ oz. consisting of three gold rings, a brooch, and some bits of broken mazers he handed back to the proctors. Raunce was described as 'of Oxford, scholar', his accomplice as 'of Oxford,

gentleman'. It is perhaps idle to think of this as an instance of town and gown partnership in crime, but it is interesting to note that Raunce was pardoned following negotiations by a university man. It is not known whether Stanshawe too had friends in the right places.

OUA WPβ/21/2/a
OUA WPα/10/1

50

A settlement of 1612

One of the periodic town–gown disputes erupted in 1609 and was finally settled by a Privy Council decree three years later. This document sets out again the perennial grievances. No. 8 of the city's complaints, for instance, was that the proctors 'doe in the night breake open and enter into the houses of well demeaning Cittizens upon sight of a Candle burning . . . and carrie them to prison'. The university, in its article no. 4, complained that the city licensed 104 alehouses 'to the Scandall of the Universitie, increase of Drunkennesse, and corrupcion of manners'. The settlement which followed was largely ineffective in resolving basic differences. One of its rulings is indicative of the balancing-act necessary. This stated that the precedency of the vice-chancellor should not be challenged, but that the mayor's authority was 'in his own kind absolute also, and in no way subordinate to the other'. Meanwhile the expenses involved in obtaining this kind of judgement were a great burden on both parties. In 1611–12 the city spent almost half its annual income on 'suits and controversies'.

OUA NEP/H/3/7

51

The 1636 university charter

This was the last of the great charters granted to the university and followed the recodification of its statutes in the same year. It both confirmed and enlarged earlier charters. Among new privileges the chancellor's court was to be a court of record, the university was to have the right to appoint its own coroners, and the town was to be inhibited from building cottages without the chancellor's leave. This was in response to the university's fears over the expansion of house-building in the town in the early part of the century. The university was given powers to hold a full court leet over the town (see no. 84), and the right to make orders and by-laws binding on townsmen in certain matters affecting the university. The charter, in extending the university's powers over the town so much, merely ensured that disputes between the two bodies would continue.

OUA Hyp./L.B./XIX

52

Expenses for the charter

The material from which the Great Charter of 1636 was drawn up was largely collected by Brian Twyne, the first Keeper of the University Archives. The mayor of the time, referring to the controversy between the university and the city, regretted that the city's lawyers would be no match for 'the antiquary who makes nothing else his study . . .'. The documents show some of Twyne's expenses on the charter: trips to London to study records involved, payments for travel, meals, accommodation, and searches, and even for having his boots cleaned. But today's citizens have cause to be thankful for this thorn in the flesh of their antecedents. Twyne's attempts to document the university's privileges involved the transcription of many of the town's medieval archives. The originals have in many cases been lost since his time (see also nos. 37–8) so that Twyne's copies are all that remain.

OUA WPα/10/5/3,9

53

The university and 'mechanicall persons'

The 1636 charter did little to resolve the perennial dispute between town and gown over precedence. These notes in the hand of Gerard Langbaine, Keeper of the University Archives and subsequently Provost of Queen's, written only a few years later, put the university's side of the case very forcibly. The first paragraph sets the tone in referring to the 'bloody experience' of the past, and further down we come to an important element in the university's attitude: 'because it is a body more considerable both in ye Church, & State, consisting of the flower of the Nobility, & Gentry of ye Kingdome, who will not indure to be subordinate to mechanicall persons'.

OUA SP/E/8/16

54

Letters of Charles I, 1642

The onset of the Civil War found the university, not surprisingly in view of the gains made as a result of Charles I's grant of a charter in 1636, loyal to the crown. Here is a contemporary copy of a letter from the king to the vice-chancellor thanking the university for a free loan of money for his defence. The other letters were sent to the mayor of Oxford and the sheriff of Oxfordshire asking them not to obey a parliamentary summons to arrest the vice-chancellor and others for assisting him. The city, while possibily not quite as enthusiastic for the king as the university, obeyed and duly published royal proclamations announcing the raising of the king's standard.

OUA SP/E/1/5, 7–8

55

Civil War coins minted at Oxford

From the king's arrival there on 29 October 1642 until the surrender of the city to the parliamentary forces on 24 June 1646, Oxford was the royalist capital of England. It housed not only the king and his court, but also the central law courts, the exchequer, parliament, and a mint. This last was established at New Inn Hall in December 1642, the equipment and officials arriving the following month. The colleges gave up their plate with only a very few attempts at evasion, and the city agreed that the citizens would give what little plate they had. This was then melted down to provide the raw material for coins. The mint remained in operation throughout the royalist occupation.

Ashm.

56

Oxford's civil war defences

This plan of the town's defences was drawn up by Sir Bernard de Gomme and is dated 13 November 1645. De Gomme was a Dutch military engineer who had accompanied Charles I's nephew, Prince Rupert, to England and, by his own account, served with the royalist army as engineer and quartermaster-general from 1642 to 1646. The drawing seems to be simply an engineer's working plan of proposed fortifications; the only details of the city shown are the castle and the churches; and of university premises, Gloucester Hall (now Worcester College), the Botanical Garden, and Christ Church. It is likely that the works shown on the plan were more or less complete by the time of the parliamentary siege in 1646.

Bodl. MS.Top.Oxon.b.167

57

City and university discussions, 1650

Town and gown dealt fairly amicably together during the Commonwealth period, but following Parliament's victory the city seems to have been encouraged to present a list of its grievances against the university in 1649. The university made a

general levy of its members to defray the expenses of a law suit. But at least the two sides entered into negotiations. This is a portion of a diary kept by Gerard Langbaine of discussions between June and August 1650 'for the concludeing of all differences now depending . . . before the Honble Committee of Parliam^{t}'. It shows part of the twenty-second meeting held on Friday 9 August, at which papers containing the 'last demands' of the city and the 'final concessions' of the university were exchanged. The two parties failed to reach agreement and were resolved to depart when 'a great shower about the time of our riseing did occasion both our and their stay till it should be over'. They eventually agreed to keep talking but the negotiations as a whole broke down shortly after and nothing was achieved.

OUA NEP/H/5/9, fol.87

58–9

The dispute of 1684

Contests over privileges continued after the Restoration. In 1684 the city tried to obtain a new charter which, among other things, would have taken St. Clement's into the city boundaries, provided for the mayor to be a county magistrate, increased the number of aldermen to eight, obtained additional markets and fairs, and limited university powers as regards policing and licensing. Some of these demands were listed in this document by John Wallis, then Keeper of the University Archives, together with the objections of the university which was naturally opposed to the demands. The copy of an order in council of 14 February 1683/4 shows that the university had royal support. In the event a new charter was obtained but it gave the city no new privileges and was annulled four years later.

OUA WPβ/R/13/3, 6

60

Arguments over precedence, 1702–3

Mayors continued to demand precedence over the vice-chancellor, and the argument reached a climax with an unseemly brawl which developed during a visit to the town by Queen Anne in 1702. By their account university members appointed to

60   Arguments over precedence, 1702-3.

meet the queen were forced 'out of their proper posts' and caused 'to ride promiscuously with the Body of the Townsmen through the High Street to the discredit of the Procession'. The messages displayed give the usual two versions of the occurrence, and also shown are some of the many documents which this single incident provoked. A complex plan to govern future processions was finally worked out later in 1703.

OUA SP/D/9

61

Bassett's case, 1759

During the course of the eighteenth century matters improved to the extent that a don could write in 1759 that a 'salutary Union' between the university and city had been established which replaced the previous 'unhappy Hostilities'. One has to be careful not to take his remarks entirely at face value. The author of this pamphlet, *The Case of a gentleman unjustly deprived of his vote*, Francis Bassett of Queen's College, wrote it to draw attention to the fact that he had been deprived of his vote in a recent university election because he had been made a freeman of the city: a too rigid interpretation (by his account) of the university statutes held this to be incompatible with the holding of academic rights and privileges. It is interesting that his opponents could still bring this argument to bear even at this late date. All was still not quite sweetness and light between town and gown.

Bodl. G.A.Oxon.8° 59(14), pp. 12-13

Reconciliation and growth in the nineteenth and twentieth centuries

From the later eighteenth century, many aspects of life in Oxford were governed by bodies on which representatives of both city and university served. This phase of shared authority lasted until 1889, when the national trend towards democratically elected local bodies led to the formation of the Oxford County Borough Council with minority university representation. For its part, the university was happy to accept a diminution of its powers since this implied also a parallel reduction in its financial responsibility for a growing city. Although the city derived benefit from its situation as a market centre, it still depended heavily upon the university as a consumer of goods and services and as a major employer until the twentieth century. The steady growth of the university and its colleges was therefore essential to the city's prosperity and it has continued to have more than just a physical impact. The development of the motor-car industry gave the city a new independence, but the rapid expansion of Oxford was accompanied by planning and traffic problems. In the modern city, old animosities between town and gown stir occasionally but have virtually disappeared.

62
Power-sharing in the town

The Oxford Improvement Act of 1771 set up a commission which included university and corporation officials as well as parish representatives and important local people to supervise the paving, cleansing, lighting, and general improvement of the town. In the next hundred years the population of Oxford trebled, putting a great administrative and financial strain on this commission, and though the Public Health Act of 1848 allowed towns to petition for a stronger local board of health, Oxford did not take the opportunity. It was not until 1864 that the Oxford Local Board of Health was established with much the same composition but with increased powers. It lasted until 1889 when it was superseded by the new Oxford County Borough Council. One of the Local Board's last achievements was the building of Osney Bridge: the bridge still bears this memorial to city and university cooperation.

OCL Photo

63
A university mayor for the city of Oxford

In 1883 the corporation and university agreed after long and difficult negotiations to seek to have

63   Alderman the Revd W. E. Sherwood, Mayor of Oxford 1913.

64 A Guy Fawkes night brawl.

Oxford made a county borough, and the Provisional Order of 1889 brought to an end much of the old diarchy by giving to the university for the first time representation on the corporation itself. The university now formed a separate ward, with nine councillors and three aldermen, forming one-fifth of the new council. Many points of difference between city and university were consequently removed, and there were several formal acts of reconciliation. At the opening of the new Town Hall in 1897

Alderman Robert Buckell became the first citizen to receive an honorary degree from the university, and in 1913 Alderman the Revd W. E. Sherwood, a former Headmaster of Magdalen Collge School, seen here in his mayoral robes, became the first university councillor to be elected mayor. University representation on the council continued until 1974, when Oxford became a district authority in the new county of Oxfordshire.

OCA D.4

64

Town and gown brawls

Although relations between city and university became generally more cordial, occasional disturbances of the peace persisted. A major outbreak of street violence occurred, for instance, during the celebrations for the end of the Crimean War in 1856, and another on the night of the opening of the new civic buildings in 1897 (see nos. 69–71). Smaller disturbances were commonplace on May Morning, the last night of Eights, and Guy Fawkes night, and provided the material for an engraving in Cuthbert Bede's novel, *The further adventures of Mr. Verdant Green*, first published in 1854. It shows Green and his associates defending themselves stoutly outside the University Church on 5 November. The fictional but realistic confrontation has the townsmen led by 'a huge lumbering bargeman' who prefaces the fight with 'brief but energetic speech, in which he delivered his opinion of Gownsmen in general, and his immediate foes in particular, in a way which would have to be expressed in proper part chiefly by blanks . . .'.

Bodl. Manning 8° 147

65–6

Reconciliation in 1955

Partnership in local government did not signal the end of petty disputes. The existence at the end of the nineteenth century of partisan newspapers and periodicals such as the *Oxford Magazine* ensured that old animosities did not die. A satirical article in that periodical on 16 March 1892 reports a fictional council debate which concludes with a plan to bring the university under city control. The twentieth century has seen a greater concentration on areas of mutual interest rather than on antag-

onism, and the 600th anniversary of St. Scholastica's Day in 1955 was marked with dignity when the mayor, Alderman W. R. Gowers, received an honorary doctorate and A. H. Smith became the first vice-chancellor to receive the freedom of the city. The scroll of his admission to the freedom of the city emphasizes the spirit of reconciliation.

Bodl. Per.G.A.Oxon.4° 141(10)
OUA WPγ/4/8

67–8

College expansion

From the eighteenth century onwards large new buildings for central university activities had changed the face of Oxford (see nos. 8–17). In the nineteenth century the increase in undergraduate numbers caused individual colleges to expand. This led not only to the development of the lodging-house (see nos. 137–8) but also to the appearance of additions to college buildings. In this activity the architect T. G. (later Sir Thomas) Jackson, fellow of Wadham College, was particularly prominent, and two of his major buildings altered the look of the city's most famous street. At the eastern end of the High Street he constructed the new Examination Schools for the university between 1877 and 1882, employing a Jacobean style which was a complete contrast to the then fashionable Gothic. It is interesting to note that Jackson was not originally amongst the five architects whom the Delegates for the New Schools wished to invite to submit designs. He was included only when E. M. Barry declined to compete.

Later, his new building for Brasenose College changed the appearance of the High Street further to the west just as comprehensively. A contemporary photograph shows this building after the completion of its first phase in 1895.

OUA UDC/M/3a/1
OCL Photo 78/6088

69–71

'A new and splendid civic palace'

This was the description given to the new Town Hall by the *Oxford Magazine* on the occasion of its opening in 1897. Replacing the eighteenth-century building visible in no. 132, the present elaborate building, designed by Henry T. Hare, symbolized the new pride of the town in its county borough status. The laying of the foundation stone on 6 July 1893 and the official opening by the Prince of Wales on 12 May 1897 were both occasions for considerable civic ceremonies and entertainment. An impressive lunch was provided on the first occasion and a great evening reception, with music under the direction of Mr C. M. Taphouse, on the second. This reception was also, unfortunately, the occasion for another of the sporadic town–gown riots which still tended to break out on joyful occasions. On this one the newly opened police cells at the Town Hall were quickly put to use, and amongst those who found themselves locked up for the night was a young Merton don — F. E. Smith, later to become Lord Birkenhead and Lord Chancellor of England.

Bodl. G.A.Oxon.b.74

72

Housing in the expanding town

As Oxford expanded attempts were made to redevelop some of the worst housing in its older parts and to develop new estates. In this movement those colleges which had been endowed with land in or on the outskirts of the town played their part. St. John's College, for example, obtained an Act of Parliament in 1855 enabling it to grant 99-year building leases over its extensive estates. This led to the development of the Walton Manor and Norham estates in the North Oxford suburb where William Wilkinson (1819–1901), a Witney-born merchant, supervised the area for the college from 1860 onwards and also designed some of the grand houses for well-to-do dons and city businessmen. This suburb is a monument to many of the architectural ideas put forward in Wilkinson's *English Country Houses* published in 1870.

By contrast Christ Church was catering for a completely different sort of lessee in the area west of Carfax. In 1866 the college ordered the demolition of tenements in St. Thomas's between The Hamel and Woodbine Place, and had them replaced by the Christ Church Model Dwellings. The three-storey block was designed by the Oxford architect Edward Bruton, and provided thirty flats with open staircases, arranged round three sides of a communal courtyard. In 1893 Christ Church built a four-storey block in Hollybush Row, known as Christ Church New Buildings. The nearby area of college-owned housing between Hollybush Row and Woodbine Place was redeveloped on building leases during the 1890s.

Bodl. G.A.Oxon.4° 180(4)

73

High church on low ground

A sermon preached by John Keble in the University Church on 14 July 1833 marked the beginning of the Oxford, or Tractarian, Movement. In their *Tracts for the Times* the protagonists emphasized the apostolic descent of the priesthood of the Church of England, the need to defend the Catholic Church, and the sanctity of the liturgy. The most conspicuous outcome of the Movement was, perhaps, the revival of ceremonial in Anglican church worship, and ritualism became a subject of fierce controversy. One of the most ritualistic churches in Oxford was that of St. Barnabas, which had been built in 1869 at the expense of Thomas Combe, superintendent of the Clarendon Press and friend of the Pre-Raphaelites, for the developing artisan suburb of Jericho. A visitor in 1876 described an Ascension Day service with a procession of acolytes carrying incense, cross and banner, and the priest in a biretta and chasuble 'stiff with gold'.

This cartoon, which depicts St. Barnabas Church as a convenient junction for converts travelling to Rome, was one of a series published photographically by Shrimptons in Oxford, and expresses some of the passion that was aroused locally. Cardinals Newman and Manning wait on the station platform. Stepping from the train is the Revd Clement Moore, first curate of St. Barnabas, who joined the Roman Catholic Church in 1872. The Revd Montague Noel was the first vicar of St. Barnabas and remained so until 1899.

Bodl. G.A.Oxon.4° 412, no. 75

74

Morris Motors Ltd.

The establishment and rapid growth of motor-car assembly at Cowley between 1910 and 1930 made Oxford a major industrial centre. This was due entirely to the success of a local man, William Morris, later Lord Nuffield, who progressed from bicycle repairs to motor-cycle manufacture and, in

1913, produced his first motor-car, the Morris Oxford. He based production at the former Oxford Military College in Cowley, and had made 1,300 cars by 1914. The firm switched to the manufacture of munitions during World War I, and car production could only expand after 1918. In 1921 Morris took the bold step of cutting car prices, and the firm's share of British car production rose from about 5 per cent in 1920 to 41 per cent in 1925. A vast factory complex was created at Cowley, and the photograph shows part of the firm's assembly line in 1933.

OCL Photo 78/6339

73   St. Barnabas Church, junction for travellers to Rome: cartoon.

74 Assembly line at Morris's Cowley factory, 1933.

75–7

The horn of plenty: Lord Nuffield as a benefactor

As a boy William Morris wanted to be a surgeon, and his life-long interest in medicine led to a remarkable series of benefactions for the advancement of medical research, teaching and practice. His first gifts in this field were made in 1927, and in 1930 he provided £100,000 for the purchase of the Radcliffe Observatory site, envisaging it as the site of an institute for medical research; in that year too, a large sum of money was provided to build a maternity home on the Radcliffe Infirmary site. In 1936 Lord Nuffield offered the university £1¼ million for the endowment of a medical school trust, providing for the establishment of three clinical departments of medicine, surgery, and obstetrics and gynaecology. The original letter making this offer was marked up for printing and circulated as a very confidential document. When Congregation met to accept the gift, Lord Nuffield unexpectedly increased his donation to £2 million, having previously expressed a wish that there should be a fourth Nuffield department, namely one in anaesthesia. Further benefactions led to the development of the Nuffield Orthopaedic Centre, and also to the creation of the college which bears his name. Shepard's cartoon in *Punch* of 2 December 1936 expressed the university's delight, and showed also the extraordinary reversal of roles by which gown now seemed a client of town, and the university 'the Latin quarter of Cowley'.

OUA SEP/5/1
OUA WPβ/7/14/3
Bodl. N.2706 d.10, vol.191

78–9

Commercial development

The population of Oxford rose from 49,336 in 1901 to 106,291 in 1961, and, with parallel growth in the Oxford region, an increase in shopping facilities became necessary. To some extent this need was met by the development of neighbourhood shopping centres in Cowley, east Oxford, Summertown, and Botley, but many changes also took place in the old city. Nowhere was this more marked than in Cornmarket Street. A photograph of the west side of the street taken on 10 July 1921 shows the double gable of Twining's Old Oxford Tea Shop (also depicted on the firm's bill-heading in no. 114) adjacent to the Clarendon Hotel. Both buildings have now disappeared. Twining's was demolished to make way for an extension to Barclays Bank in 1921, and the Clarendon Hotel was pulled down in 1955 following a lengthy and bitterly contested planning controversy, and replaced with a large Woolworth store built to this design by Sir William Holford. Further expansion of a confined shopping area was considered necessary by the 1960s, and the Westgate Shopping Centre was built between 1969 and 1973.

Bodl. Minn neg. 4/4
OCL Illustration

80

Roads and planning

A relief road from Walton Well Road to Botley Road was suggested in the 1880s, and the Donnington Bridge proposal mooted by the City Council in 1922 also had its origins in the nineteenth century. Oxford traffic problems were, however, greatly exacerbated in the 1920s by the city's growth and the increasing popularity of the motor-car. The Council accepted a scheme which proposed a ring of bypasses in 1925, and in the 1930s the northern bypass was built to keep traffic on the A40 to the north of the city. A section of the southern bypass was constructed between Botley and Hinksey Hill in 1932, but completion of the ring road was delayed until 1965. The subject of inner relief roads has been much more controversial, and the Christ Church Meadow road, proposed by Lawrence Dale in 1941, excited powerful opposition mainly from within the university. Merton Mall, as it was at one time called, was supported in 1948 by the City Council's planning consultant, Thomas Sharp, who argued in his book *Oxford Replanned* (1948) that it would make little impact on the Meadow — a view obviously not shared by J. C. (later Sir John) Masterman, Provost of Worcester College, whose copy of Sharp's book is shown here. The debate extended over many years until the plan was abandoned in 1968.

Lent by a private owner

81

The Oxford Preservation Trust

The rapid growth of twentieth-century Oxford was seen by many in the city and the university as posing a threat to Oxford's beauty. The moving spirit behind the creation of the Oxford Preservation Trust in 1927 was H. A. L. Fisher, Warden of New College, and the trust soon found allies both in the colleges and in the city. Money was raised by donations and subscriptions, and in February 1930 a special matinee was held on the trust's behalf at the New Theatre. Contributions to the souvenir programme of this occasion included a witty letter from Evelyn Waugh, who suggested that the trust might embark upon the judicious destruction of bridges and ugly buildings, and thus create a quieter and more beautiful city, 'undisturbed except for the brawling of the dons'. In fact the trust was founded with the intention of 'so guiding the development of Oxford as to preserve and increase the beauty of the city and of its surrounding neighbourhood'. It swiftly adopted a policy of purchasing important sites endangered by development, and offered suggestions and architectural advice for the harmonious treatment of sites and buildings in the city and neighbourhood. It has expressed conservationist views on many planning issues, including notably the Green Belt and Oxford road schemes, and now occupies offices in nos. 8–10 Turnagain Lane, seventeenth-century buildings which it saved from demolition in 1971.

Oxford Preservation Trust Records

3 COMMUNITY LIFE

Jurisdiction and peace-keeping

A continuing source of friction between city and university was the existence of two separate jurisdictions within the town, that of the mayor and bailiffs on the one hand and that of the university's chancellor on the other. The earliest reference to a town court occurs in about 1130, and with the growth of Oxford's privileges in this and the succeeding century its competence and jurisdiction gradually increased. By the late thirteenth century there were two clearly defined town courts, the Monday Court presided over by the bailiffs and dealing with breaches of the king's peace, assault, bloodshed, and actions involving real property, and the Friday Court of the mayor which dealt with offences against market and craft regulations and small debts. With some changes these courts continued to be held until the nineteenth century.

Trouble arose because of the parallel rise of the chancellor's court, which came into existence at the same time as the office of chancellor around 1214. This was an ecclesiastical court whose jurisdiction was primarily over the university's scholars, but there were bound to be difficulties in cases involving both clerks and non-scholars. Associated with this was the question as to exactly who should enjoy the privileges of the university. Various charters and agreements attempted to delineate the jurisdictions and define who could be 'a privileged person', but disputes between town and gown over these points continued into the seventeenth century. The position was complicated further since some townsmen found it useful to have access to the chancellor's court, particularly to recover debts.

After the seventeenth century the chancellor's court lost most of its power and gradually became almost exclusively concerned with debt cases, chiefly of townsmen trying to recover money from undergraduates. It was scarcely used in the twentieth century although it was not finally abolished until 1977.

There were similar difficulties over a dual system of courts leet, which heard complaints about and levied fines for nuisances and failure to repair streets. Both city and university had leets in the sixteenth and seventeenth centuries with an inevitable conflict of interest.

The university had established by the early sixteenth century the right to patrol the streets of Oxford by night ('the night watch') and this was another activity about which university and city did not always see eye to eye, especially when the university's officials, the proctors, were held to be exceeding their rights. Not until the nineteenth century did this cease to be a cause of friction. Separate university and city police forces were formed then and they continued to divide peace-keeping responsibilities in the town between them until their amalgamation in 1869.

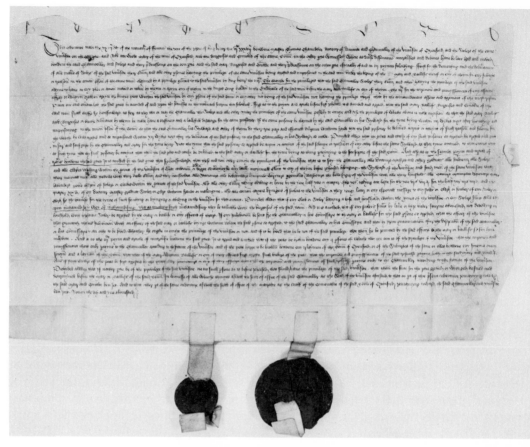

82 Privileged persons: agreement of 1459.

82

Privileged persons

An agreement of 1290 between the town and the university first defined those eligible to share the privileges of the university, later known as privileged persons. These were people who, while not scholars, were matriculated and were enabled to claim exemption from the town's jurisdiction since they came under that of the chancellor. Acquisition of privileged status was one way in which a non-freeman might practise a trade in the town. Disputes over allowable categories of privileged persons were frequent and in 1459 the further agreement between town and university displayed here was made. Its immediate cause was the trouble which had arisen in the previous year when the chancellor had punished a bailiff for imprisoning a scholar. As well as settling certain points at issue concerning town and university jurisdictions, it also sets out once again the allowable categories of privileged persons. In addition to all scholars and their servants the list also includes members of certain trades closely linked with the university: stationers, bookbinders, parchment-makers, cooks, launderers, barbers, and carriers, among others. The document is in English and bears the seals of the town of Oxford and of the mayor. The chancellor of the university was Thomas Chaundler who is pictured in no. 47.

OUA WPβ/L/3

83
A scholar's 'servant'

Despite the 1459 agreement the status of privileged persons continued to be abused, and until the beginning of the seventeenth century the town was constantly complaining about the university's extension of the privilege to an ever-wider range of occupations. Already by 1524 about a fifth of the town's taxable inhabitants were privileged persons. This extract from the first chancellor's court register, dated 13 October 1466, records that John Coke '*in legibus doctor*' took as his servant Thomas Havylde. Havylde or Haville was a leading brewer who had been a bailiff in 1458. Quite prominent men might find privileged status convenient and it is possible that Haville's purpose was to facilitate the recovery of debts in the chancellor's court.

OUA Reg. Aaa, Hyp./A/1, fol.294

OUA Reg. Aaa, Hyp./A/1, fol.294ᵛ

84
The court leet

In the early sixteenth century the university claimed the right to hold a court leet twice a year in the guild hall, to which the town bailiffs were expected to summon a jury of eighteen townsmen. The leet had not been granted by charter, but resulted from the transfer to the university of the assize of bread and ale in 1355 (see no. 39). Consequently its jurisdiction included weights and measures and corn prices in addition to the presentments of nuisances and street repairs which make up a large part of this extract from the leet held on 20 October 1596. Fines for failing to pave dominate here, but there are presentments of other nuisances such as the dunghill kept by Mr Alderman Rowe at his garden wall, for which he was fined 12d. The town was strongly opposed to the university leet since it had its own leet, and it frequently refused to empanel a satisfactory jury or refused access to the guild hall. The university leet fell into disuse after the Restoration, but the city's leet survived until 1839.

OUA WPβ/C/6

85
'The night watch'

The university's right to patrol the streets of the town at night was well established by the early sixteenth century but this did not prevent the town complaining bitterly at intervals about the actions of individual proctors. In 1609 the right to police the town became a central issue when a bailiff, Richard Painter, was fined £20 by the vice-chancellor for the exercise of the night walk 'under pretence of searching for felons', and then imprisoned until the fine was paid. This document is signed by the mayor, Thomas Harryes, and touches on this and several other disputes over jurisdiction. It contains an acknowledgment that the night watch 'belongeth onely to the university' and that if any bailiff performed it without the vice-chancellor's leave 'be it at his owne perill'. The quarrel ended in 1612 when the Privy Council ruled that the watch belonged to the university but that the bailiffs should be allowed to pursue their reasonable business at night (see no. 50).

86
No dumping

The authorities in most sixteenth- and seventeenth-century towns were concerned with the control of disease caused by insanitary conditions. In Oxford this led to cooperation between town and gown in attempts to control rubbish disposal, a problem not unknown today, although the actual items concerned are a little different. A printed order of 1661 over the names of both vice-chancellor and mayor admonishes all inhabitants that 'they carry not out into the adjacent High-wayes or Fields . . . and leave the same uncovered, any the Carcasses of Dead Horses, Hogges, Dogges, or the like . . .'. The university and city also cooperated in the appointment of a scavenger in the seventeenth century, and both made regulations about street repairs and cleaning, although this often led to disputes about which body was entitled to receive the fines paid by offenders.

OUA WPγ/28/8, no.14

87–8
The university and the city gaol

The vice-chancellor as a magistrate had long had the power to commit prisoners to the city gaol. By the nineteenth century in practice these were mainly prostitutes. An 1824 Act of Parliament altered the law so as to permit the imprisonment of prostitutes only for 'riotous or indecent behaviour', whereas the university had committed them merely on detection as 'rogues and vagabonds'. This letter from the mayor protests that great expense would fall on the city if the university continued to operate under the old law. A committee was set up to look into the expenditure on the city gaol and the second document shows part of its findings. An agreement was reached in 1826; the university was to retain its 'indiscriminate power of commitment', but undertook part of the financial burden, 10d. a day to be paid to the city for every woman imprisoned as a common prostitute by the vice-chancellor.

OUA NEP/A/7/1, 5

89
The university police

The university's right to control the 'night watch' continued into the nineteenth century and in 1829 it set up its own properly constituted police force. It consisted of two inspectors and sixteen constables, who had full jurisdiction over the city from 9 p.m. to 4 a.m. Shown here are extracts from the set of printed instructions issued on the establishment of the force, setting out the duties and responsibilities of inspectors and constables.

OUA WPβ/5/23

90
An inspector's report

An inspector of the university police was required to keep a report book in which he was to enter up all the night's occurrences. This one is open at the events of the nights of Christmas Eve and Christmas Day 1865, and, as might be expected at this time of year, relates exclusively to cases of drunkenness in various parts of the town. It would appear that at least one of the constables, notwithstanding his strict instructions to remain sober while on duty, was filled with Christmas spirit in more ways than one.

Bodl. MS.Top.Oxon.b.159, fols.4ᵛ–5

91–2
Police truncheons

Members of both the university and the city police forces carried truncheons. One of those shown here belonged to Abner Savage, who was a university police inspector 1844–68, the other to Henry Minn as a special constable in the city force 1914–19.

Ashm.

93
The city police

Before 1835 the city was policed during the day by a number of constables appointed by the corporation. The city and its suburbs were divided into sections, which by and large coincided with parish boundaries, each having a head who organized the constables within his area. Shown here is the set of instructions for heads of sections in 1830. Despite these efforts at organization the system was not particularly effective, the Anti-Mendicity Society at this time going so far as to employ its own constables to keep the street clear of vagrants. In 1836 a municipal police force was set up under the Municipal Corporations Act, consisting of a superintendent, two inspectors, eight constables and two supernumeraries. They worked from 4 a.m. to 9 p.m., then handed over to their opposite numbers in the university force for the night, exchanging any information that might be useful at the change-over.

Bodl. G.A.Oxon.c.46, no.121

94
The amalgamated force

The dual system of policing Oxford came under criticism in the mid-nineteenth century for being inefficient. Moreover, this sort of involvement in the administration of a growing city was becoming a costly affair for the university, and in 1864 it began to negotiate for the amalgamation of the city and university police forces. The city, understandably, was not anxious to assume this extra financial burden and negotiations dragged on until 1866, when the university notified the council that unless the matter was put to arbitration it would discontinue the night watch except for its own purposes. Amalgamation was finally achieved in 1869, with the university making a substantial contribution to the cost of the new force. This initially consisted of a superintendent, two inspectors, and thirty-two constables, and was administered by a committee containing both city and university representatives. The corporation assumed full control of the police in 1889, by which time its strength was sixty-two. The Oxford City Police Force survived until 1968 when it became part of the Thames Valley Force. The photograph shows police on duty at a college commemoration ball in 1914.

OCL Photo

Dec.r 25th & 26th Monday Night

N.o 1 off duty; Supt.n N.o 1 sent on his Beat.

N.o 2 off duty; Supt.n N.o 2 sent on his Beat.

N.o 3 unwell, Supt.n N.o 3 sent on his Beat

Inspected the Men with the assistant Sub-Inspector at ½ past Nine o'Clock in at a ¼ before Two ——

The Inspector reports Supt.n N.o 3 (Giles) who was found shut in his Box drunk and incapable of doing his duty, he was sent home at 20 minutes before Two o'Clock ——

N.o 8

95

The proctors

Even after 1869 the university proctors preserved some of their powers in the town, and for a time at any rate continued to arrest prostitutes and vagrants at night as they had done under the old system and bring them before the vice-chancellor. This system remained unchanged, though little used, until 1968, when all *ex officio* justices of the peace, who included the vice-chancellor, lost their places. The proctors still retain powers of discipline over members of the university and the object and notices displayed relate to just one of these.

After World War I there was an upsurge in the numbers of undergraduates driving cars and the university sought to control their use. A proctorial licence was necessary for an undergraduate to maintain a car in Oxford during term time and cars had to be kept in licensed garages so that a check could be kept on their use; they were not to be driven in the mornings, when undergraduates were supposed to be pursuing their studies, nor after midnight. Since it was not always easy for the proctors to distinguish between an undergraduate's vehicle and that of a townsman, in 1927 it was decreed that a small green lamp be affixed to undergraduates' cars. These lamps were no longer obligatory after 1966/7.

OUA Proctors' records

The university and the city: trade and employment

Before the coming of the motor-car Oxford was not noted as a manufacturing centre. If its enterprise was not engaged in supplying goods to the world at large, however, a town with a large university in its midst was primarily engaged in providing for the needs of its local consumers, and commerce flourished. Certain trades in particular, such as those practised by the brewers, the mercers, tailors, drapers and outfitters, the chandlers, grocers, barbers, and apothecaries, the masons and builders, and those who made and sold books have prospered. It is significant, for instance, that in the sixteenth century about three-quarters of the taxpayers were engaged in the victualling, distributive, clothing, and building trades, and a further fifth were employed directly by the university. This compares with about 40 per cent engaged in those trades in comparable towns such as Leicester or Northampton.

As a captive body of consumers the university had always felt in need of some protection against the town's traders, and after 1355 (see no. 39) it gained control of the price and quality of food and of the market. From this basis the university extended its powers into other areas of trade. It claimed the right, for example, to license both those who sold ale and those who sold wine in the town. In the fifteenth century categories of 'privileged persons' were recognized who shared in the university's rights and were subject to its jurisdiction (see no. 82), and certain guilds, such as those of the barbers and the cooks, were controlled by the university although the town successfully resisted attempts at university control of others.

The increased demand in the eighteenth and nineteenth centuries for luxury goods encouraged the growth of large and well-stocked retail shops which catered for these needs often on the basis of long-term credit, while the increased population and expansion of buildings in the same period led to the corresponding growth in the number of people employed directly by the colleges.

Most of the university's jurisdiction over trade lapsed or was abolished in the nineteenth century. It still provides employment and a ready market for the craft skills and commercial acumen of many townsmen, but its importance in this respect, too, has declined with the expansion of Oxford in the twentieth century as an industrial centre.

96

The assize of bread

In medieval times special courts existed to control the size and standard of loaves of bread, and the quality of ale. The right to hold these 'assizes' of bread and of ale was granted to the university following the St. Scholastica's Day riot of 1355 (see no. 39), but even before that date the university as a major consumer had won the right to be represented at the meetings of the court. The record for the assize of bread held in September and October 1337 shows it being held under the joint jurisdic-

tion of Robert de Stretforde, chancellor of the university, and Henry de Stodeleighe, mayor of Oxford. It gives the names of those fined for selling short-weight bread, and the amounts which they had to pay. Loaves had various names such as *wastell*, *coket* and *clermatyn*. The assize was not abolished until 1836.

OUA SEP/Y/16, rot.16

97

The assize of weights and measures

In any trading community there is an obvious need for the control of weights and measures. This control in Oxford, again known as the 'assize' of weights and measures, was another of the privileges acquired by the university in 1355. Offenders were punished by the university court leet (see no. 84). Standard sets of weights were kept against which to check those used by local tradespeople. They were renewed periodically and the last set, dated 1778 and 1826, remained in use until 1965. Control was transferred to the city in 1869 when the enforcement of the weights and measures regulations passed to the police committee.

OCM

98–9

Brewing

The university's control of the assize of ale gradually gave it control of brewing in Oxford in the fifteenth and sixteenth centuries. It also encouraged the brewers to act as a corporate body. From 1434 onwards the university laid down a rota which named the days on which individual brewers should brew. This was an attempt to regulate the supply of ale. Attempts to enforce this rota were never completely successful and when, in 1500–1, by the regulation shown here, a longer rota was introduced in order to favour the poorer brewers, it had to be abandoned since it simply led to a shortage of ale. The names of twenty-one brewers are given at the foot of the page.

By the second half of the seventeenth century brewers no longer needed university approval. They were, however, still extremely important in the economic life of Oxford. Manciples regularly spent large sums of money on beer for their colleges and still used the medieval system of acknowledging debts by using wooden tallies. The ten tallies shown here were issued one per quarter by the manciple of St. Mary Hall from 1669 to 1672. The number of barrels of beer supplied by the brewer is indicated by the notches on the edge of the tally. The price, and any payment, is written on its face.

OUA Reg. α Hyp./A/2, fols. 104ᵛ–105
OUA Tallies from Chancellor's Court Papers 1676

100

Licences to sell ale or beer

A list drawn up by the university in 1640 of those who were licensed to sell ale or beer. The right to

license such persons was claimed by the university as an extension of its control of the assize of bread and ale, but it was disputed both by the town and on occasion by those who had received royal patents allowing them to license additional alehouses. It was, however, confirmed by the university's charter in 1636. Both city and university tried to restrict licensing but the number of inns and alehouses in the city increased. In 1678 alehouses numbered about 370; in 1830 there were at least 136 public houses and 13 inns and posting-houses. With about 400 licensed premises in 1844, Oxford had one for every sixty inhabitants.

OUA WPβ/15/9/25

101

Wine licences

An eighteenth-century bottle which contained wine sold by one of Oxford's taverns has a seal bearing the emblem of the tavern from which it came: the Three Tuns. It also carries the name of the then proprietor, A. Tomlinson (Ann Tomlinson, who ran the tavern from 1712 to 1719) and the date, 1713. The Three Tuns existed from about 1650 to 1750. The building of which it formed a part was in the High Street and can be seen clearly in Ralph Agas's map (no. 5) as a four-storied building with dormers opposite All Souls College. Part of University College now occupies the site.

The number of those who could be licensed to sell wine in Oxford was restricted to three by an Act of 1553. Both the university and the city claimed the right to issue the three licences and did so. On occasion, therefore, there were six vintners, although some men obtained licences from both bodies. The university continued to license wine retailers until the late nineteenth century. The city no longer granted licences after the middle of the eighteenth century, and the nature of the trade was in any case changing at that period, when colleges began to lay down their own cellars and the traditional trade of the taverns declined in the face of competition from newly established wine-vaults.

Ashm.

102

A chandler

From the medieval period onwards there were men who lived in both the world of the university and

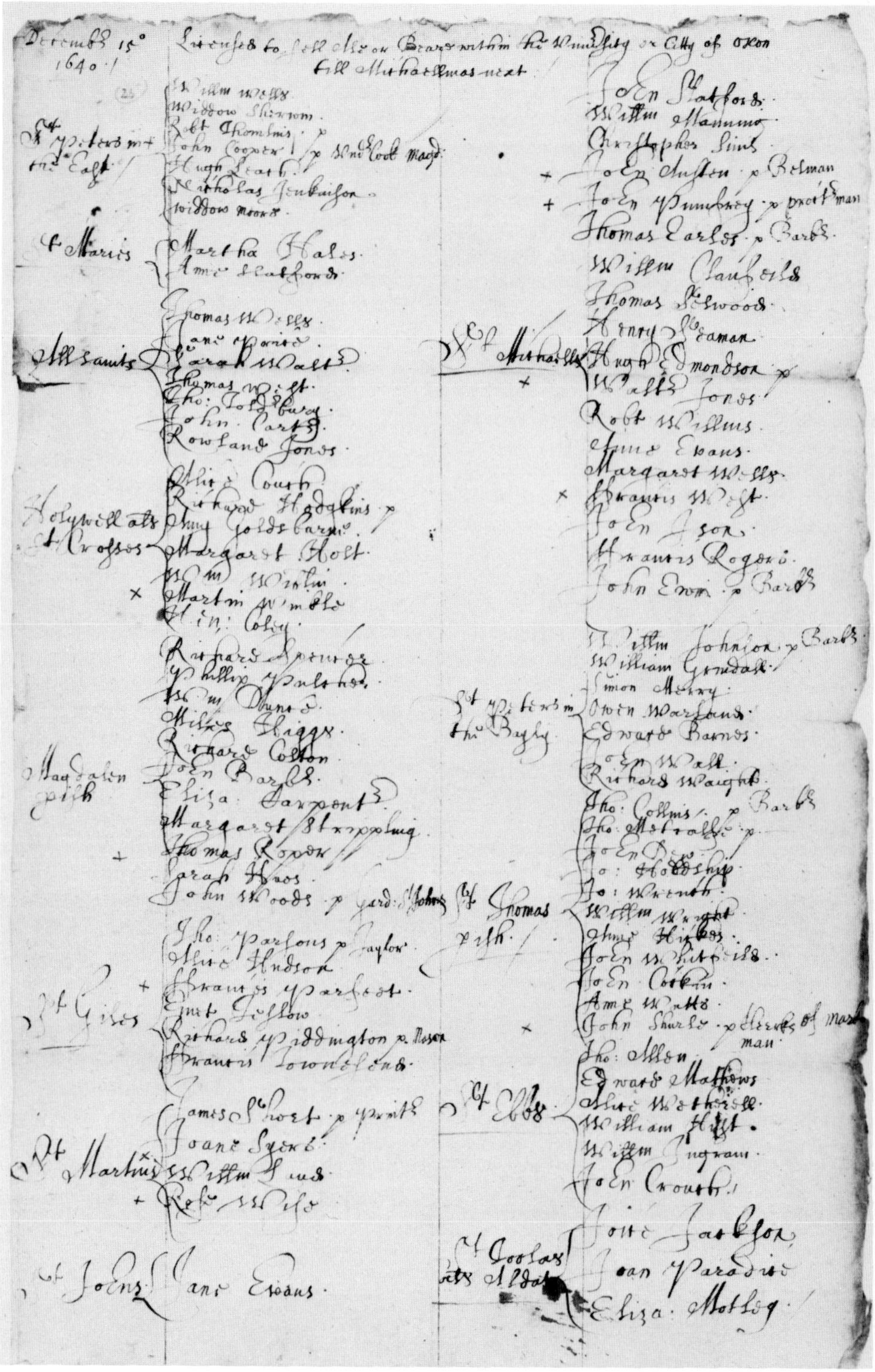
Decemb 15° 1640 — Licenses to sell Ale or Beare within the University or Citty of Oxon till Michaelmas next

St Peters in the East: Willm Wells, Widdow Shirrom, Robt Thomlins p, John Cooper p Wnd Cook Magd, Hugh Leath, Nicholas Jenkinson, Widdow Moore.

St Maries: Martha Hales, Anne Stafford.

All saints: Thomas Wells, Jane Sparke, Sarah Walt, Thomas Wright, Tho: Tolkbury, John Carte, Rowland Jones.

Holywell als St Crosses: Alice Couch, Richard Hodgkins p, Ann Goldsbarne, Margaret Holt, Wm Witlin, Martin Wimble, Hen Colby.

Magdalen pish: Richard Spencer, Phillip Walcher, Wm Dunce, Miles Skiggs, Richard Colton, John Barkb, Eliza Carpenter, Margaret Strippling, Thomas Roper, Sarah Hoos, John Woods p Gard St Johns.

St Giles: Tho: Parsons p Taylor, Alice Hudson, Francis Barefoot, Emit Ieltow, Richard Widdington p Mason, Francis Townsend.

St Martins: James Short p Print, Joane Syers, Willm Sims, Robt Wilde.

St Johns: Jane Evans.

St Michaells: John Stafford, Willm Manning, Christopher Sims, John Austen p Belman, John Humfrey p Pritt man, Thomas Earles p Barb, Willm Clanfeild, Thomas Selwood, Henry Seaman, Hugh Edmondson p, Walter Jones, Robt Willms, Anne Evans, Margaret Wells, Francis Wright, John Ison, Francis Rogers, John Ervin p Barb.

St Peters in the Baily: Willm Johnson p Barb, William Grindall, Simon Merry, Owen Warford, Edward Barnes, John Walt, Richard Wright, Tho: Collins p Barb, Tho: Metcalfe p, John Dew, Jo: Holdship, Jo: Wrench.

St Thomas pish: Willm Wright, Anne Hibbs, John Whitfeild, John Corkin, Amy Watts, John Sharle p Clerke of Marsh man, Tho: Allen.

St Ebbs: Edward Mathews, Alice Wetherell, William Hilst, Willm Ingram, John Crouch.

St Tooles als Aldat: Joice Jackson, Joan Paradise, Eliza Motley.

100 Licences to sell ale or beer, 1640.

that of the town. They were tradesmen who also served college offices. Many innkeepers, for instance, were also college cooks or butlers, and college manciples almost always had other strings to their bows in the town. One such man was James Pen who died in 1642. He was manciple of St. John's College and was also a substantial city chandler with a well-stocked shop and workhouse in the High Street. As can be seen from the inventory of his goods drawn up at his death, his shop contained a wide variety of goods ranging from spices to haberdashery, from drinking glasses and jugs to soap, and from blue to anchovies. In a cellar he kept a large and valuable stock of currants, raisins, vinegar, and salt. His candle manufactory was in a detached workhouse where he had a boiler and firing and many hundredweights of tallow. His contacts with the university were not only on the trading front, for he married the niece of a President of Corpus Christi College.

Bodl. MS.Wills Oxon.171/3/22

103

Market proclamations

The proclamation issued by Archbishop Laud, chancellor of the university, in 1634 is one of a series covering all aspects of market jurisdiction issued from the mid-fifteenth century onwards. The right to publish such proclamations had been given to the university by the charter of 1355 and was confirmed by that of 1636, and it continued to publish them until the eighteenth century. This one shows the university enforcing its control of weights and measures and the licensing of ale-houses. It also shows its attempts to regulate the activities of chandlers such as James Pen (no. 102). The university claimed control over chandlers as suppliers of food and drink in Oxford, but artificial light, which the chandlers were mainly in business to supply, was expensive in the seventeenth century, and both townsmen and scholars were con-

104 High Street, north side: copy by J. Buckler of eighteenth-century drawing.

[43]

stantly worried about the scarcity of tallow and the rising price of candles. It was through these proclamations, therefore, that the university attempted to regulate the supply and the price of this necessary commodity.

OUA WPγ/28/8, no.5

104–7

The Covered Market

The market over which the university had gained control by the 1355 charter was held until the eighteenth century in the streets radiating out from Carfax, often on stalls set out by tradesmen in front of their shops. The houses and shops on the north side of the High Street running down from Carfax are shown in an early eighteenth-century drawing copied by John Buckler. The 1771 Improvement Act, however, recognized the need for a separate market to relieve the congestion in the streets, and the joint city and university commission established under the Act proceeded to construct the Covered Market. The sixth edition of *The New Oxford Guide* published in 1776 shows a plan and elevation of the new market, while the description claimed that it was 'universally allowed to exceed every thing of the kind in this kingdom'.

The profits from the market were to be divided evenly between the university and the town, and the 1771 Act provided for the continued appointment by the university of Clerks of the Market (a title first used in 1513) to control it. The university lost its direct share in this control upon the creation of the new borough council in 1889 though it still appoints Clerks of the Market. Their sole remaining duty is to ascertain twice a year the price of corn and to announce it at the annual corn rent dinner of estates bursars, since this is still the basis for certain college rents. In 1909, when Dr C. H. O. Daniel, Provost of Worcester, was clerk, the duties still included checking the weight of butter, the main item in the market then sold as of a given weight (rather than being weighed out when sold to the customer).

Bodl. MS.Don.a.2, no.44
Bodl. G.A.Oxon.8° 347 and 347*
J. Betjeman & D. Vaisey, Victorian and Edwardian Oxford from old photographs (1971), no.33

108

Barbers

The barbers' trade was, like brewing (see nos. 98–9) and tailoring (see nos. 45–6), especially associated with the university and was controlled by it. A guild was established as early as 1348 and its regulation by the university over the years met with little opposition from the town. This guild, following a period of decline, was re-established as the Company of Barbers of the University of Oxford in 1675 and its ordinances inscribed in an order book. All barbers from then on were required to be matriculated into the university. Not all of them, however, obeyed the regulations, and an order dated 24 March 1725/6, shown here, indicates that some were employing 'in Chambers, Garrets, and other private Places' persons who were not members of the Company to make 'Perukes, Borders, or Artificial Heads of Hair' which they then sold illegally. By the nineteenth century the Company had become virtually non-effective and was dissolved by the university at the request of the barbers in 1859.

Bodl. MS.Oxford Barbers 3, fol.22

109

Discommoning

The university's ultimate sanction against a townsman who transgressed the regulations of a trade over which it exercised control, was discommoning. This in effect forbade colleges, scholars, or privileged persons to trade with, or have anything to do with, the person discommoned. The consequent loss of trade could be a serious blow to someone whose business depended mainly on university custom, and could lead to his ruin.

The wording of the printed discommoning notice was severe and, evidently, it was often other members of the trade rather than the university authorities who took the initiative in getting the notice published. William Wise, a matriculated stationer, was discommoned in June 1804 for using his position as a stationer as a way of trying to get into the business of bookselling. The pamphlet *An Appeal from custom to conscience* which he wrote in his own defence sharply attacked the established booksellers who sought to close him down when they themselves, so he claimed, unscrupulously sold all sorts of stationery.

Bodl. 2581 f.31, pp.6–7

110

Credit in Oxford

From the seventeenth century onwards surviving documents show that most university members expected to be able to purchase goods on credit. In Oxford perhaps more than in many other towns, therefore, credit was easily available and undergraduates were able to run up large debts. Although debtors could always be pursued in the chancellor's court, the situation was not made easier by the fact that many were still minors. Tailors were particularly vulnerable. *A Few general directions for the conduct of young gentlemen in the University of Oxford* which was published in 1795 sarcastically attacked undergraduates who insisted on having all the most up-to-date clothes and goods regardless of cost, and treated tradesmen as if 'they are such for the express ends of being ruined by giving credit'. Elsewhere the writer states: 'You cannot show your face without owning such necessaries as thirteen or fourteen Coats, three or four dozen of Waistcoats, and as many pairs of Breeches.'

Bodl. G.A.Oxon.8° 219(7), pp.4–5

111–12

Undergraduate debt

Two bills show debts run up by undergraduates who subsequently became national figures. D. Haig of Brasenose College, subsequently Field Marshal the Earl Haig, was pursued by a livery-stable keeper for expenses largely in connection with his activities as a polo-player in 1882, while C. B. Fry's debts from 1891 to 1893 to H. Kelson and Sons of 46 Holywell Street reflect the all-round sporting and academic activities of an extraordinarily gifted young man.

OUA Chancellor's Court Papers, 1883, no.59
OUA Chancellor's Court Papers, 1893, no.80

113

The collection of debts

Many tradesmen, as an inducement to quick payment, either offered a discount for cash or threatened to impose 5 per cent interest on amounts unpaid after one year. This latter sanction

was not always used, as can be seen in the Kelson bill in no. 112. If payment were delayed for too long, however, the debtor could be summoned into the chancellor's court which by the nineteenth century had, in fact, become primarily a court for the recovery of such debts. One debtor in 1877 was Oscar Wilde, then an undergraduate at Magdalen College, who had failed to settle a bill for masonic regalia bought from the shop of G. H. Osmond in St. Aldate's. In a characteristic letter to the court Wilde voiced a feeling of grievance over the expense to which he was liable to be put in settling what he considered a 'monstrous claim', arguing that a court which could charge such fees 'must be conducted on a system which requires the investigation of the University Commission'.

OUA Chancellor's Court Papers 1877, no.98

114

Shops and shopkeeping

The flourishing retail trade during the nineteenth and twentieth centuries is illustrated by a selection of bill-headings, paper bags, and other advertising ephemera. Spiers and Son was a particularly well-known fancy-goods shop in the High Street in the years before its closure in 1889. Its brightly coloured *Memorial for visitors to Oxford* was given away to customers as a keepsake.

Some of the shops are instantly recognizable from the illustrations or wording on their bill-headings, though others have now vanished. Products such as Frank Cooper's Oxford marmalade carried the name of Oxford into the consumer world at large. Other traders catered much more specifically for university needs: Woodward and Richmond, for example, predecessors of the present Shepherd and Woodward, were specialists in academic robes.

Bodl. John Johnson Collection
OUA Chancellor's Court papers
OCM

115–16

Banking

Flourishing banks have existed in Oxford since the eighteenth century. The exact date of the establishment of the Old Bank is not known. It was operated

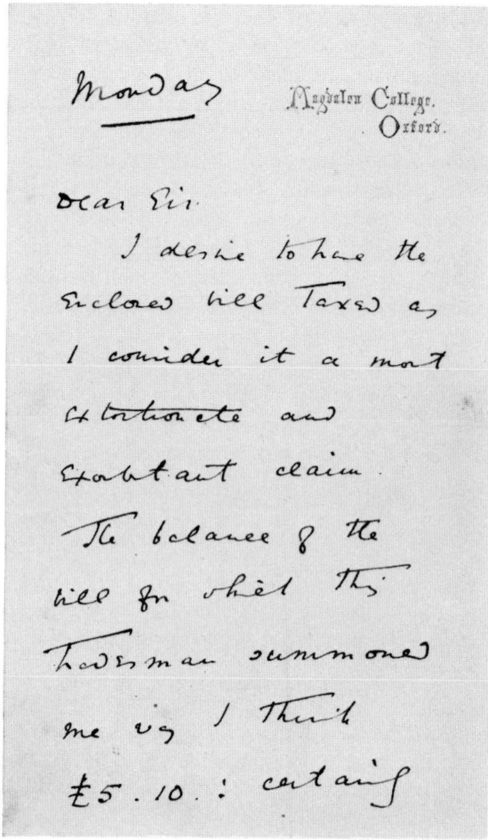

Monday *Magdalen College.*
Oxford.

Dear Sir

 I desire to have the enclosed bill Taxed, as I consider it a most extortionate and exorbitant claim.

The balance of the bill for which this Tradesman summoned me is, I think £5.10.: certainly a good deal under six – and it allows to be that if nearly £3 costs are allowed on a £5 bill, the Vice Chancellor Court must be conducted on a system. which requires the investigation of the University Commission:

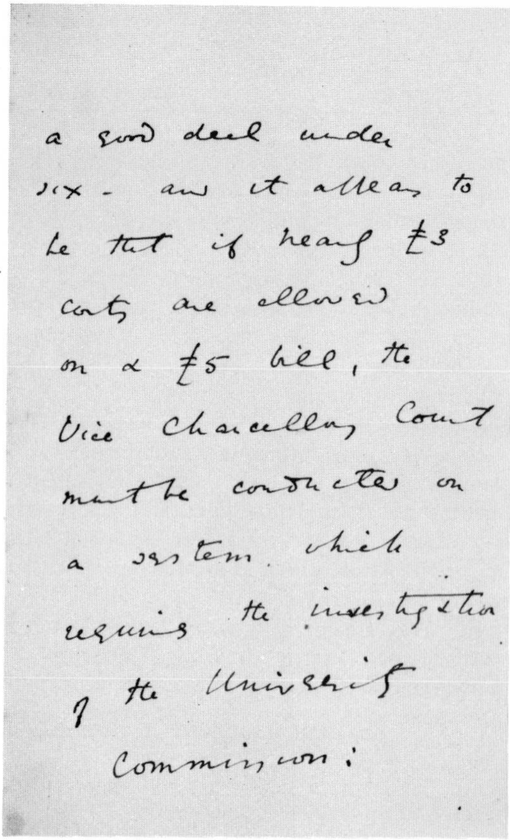

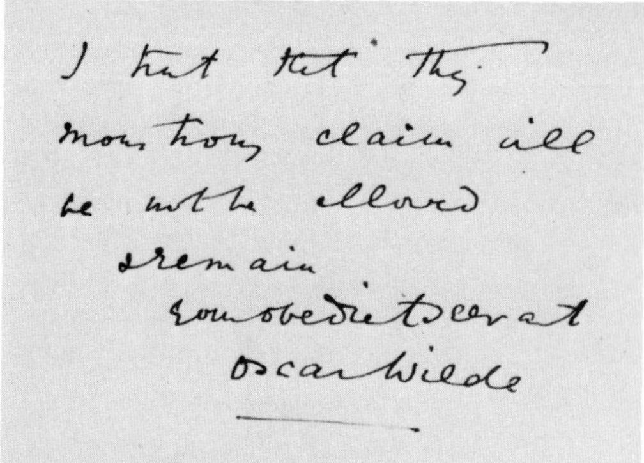

I trust that this monstrous claim will not be allowed

   I remain

    your obedient servant

    Oscar Wilde

113 Oscar Wilde's prosecution for debt: letter to the court.

by William Fletcher (see no. 119) and John Parsons, both of whom started as tradesmen and mercers and went on to become bankers. While still mercers they went into partnership in 1775. By 1790 the banking side of the business was known as The Old Bank to distinguish it from two other banks then operating in Oxford. From then onwards the banking activity grew steadily and the mercery finally ended in 1808. It was amalgamated with Barclays Bank in 1900. The accounts showed a strong university and professional connection, which remained throughout the bank's life. The ledger covering the years 1790–1816 is shown here together with a £5 note which the bank issued. The account is that of a university client — William Cowderoy, janitor of the Bodleian Library.

Barclays Bank, Old Bank, High Street
OCM

114   Retail trading, nineteenth–twentieth centuries: ephemera from Oxford shops.

117

One of the Old Bank's customers

A catalogue of the several pictures, statues, and busts, in the picture gallery, Bodleian Library, and Ashmolean Museum at Oxford, Oxford, 1806, was sold by William Cowderoy whose bank account is shown as no. 115. Cowderoy was janitor at the Bodleian Library from *c.* 1785 until *c.* 1826. He almost certainly augmented his income with fees for showing people round the Library and the picture gallery and sales of this catalogue. The items listed on the pages shown could be seen in the picture gallery (now the Upper Reading Room of the Library).

Bodl. Bliss B.149, pp.6–7

118–19

Books

The presence of the university in Oxford has from the earliest days meant that there has been a flourishing business in the town concerned with writing, making, binding, printing, and selling books. The earliest English professional illuminator known by name worked in Oxford in a tenement in Catte Street where All Souls College now is, a street housing many craftsmen engaged in the book trade (see no. 31). He was William de Brailes, who illuminated this small bible in *c.* 1230.

The oil painting by William Green shows the book trade in operation in Oxford some five hundred years later in 1747. An auction is depicted and it was evidently attended mainly by scholars. The picture is known to have hung in the house of Alderman William Fletcher, where the New Bodleian Library stands now, and probably shows the establishment of Fletcher's father James in Turl Street. James Fletcher in 1731 founded the bookselling business which at the end of the eighteenth century became Parker's.

Bodl. MS.Lat.bib.e.7
Bodl. Picture

120–2

A bookselling establishment

It was on 1 January 1879 that Benjamin Henry Blackwell, son of Benjamin Harris Blackwell, the first Oxford city librarian, opened his bookshop at 50 Broad Street and in the same month issued his first catalogue of secondhand books which included as no. 422 a fine copy of Loggan's *Oxonia Illustrata*, 1675, for £5. In those days the shop was so small that if more than three customers were present, the apprentice had to stand in the street. From these small beginnings the vast Blackwell bookselling concern has been built by Benjamin Henry, his son Sir Basil Henry, and his sons and grandsons. If Blackwells is now a household word throughout the book-buying world, then so is the name of Sir Basil, 'the Gaffer', the recipient of the highest honours that both city and university can bestow — the honorary freedom of the former and an honorary doctorate of the latter. At the degree

ceremony the Public Orator referred to him as 'Jupiter of the Booksellers'.

OUA NW/9/75
Bodl. G.A.Oxon.8° 1798
Bodl. 2593 e.133ª

123–5

An Oxford family and its brewery

One of the most powerful Oxford families over the past two hundred years has been that which descended from Jeremiah Morrell of Wallingford, who died in 1766. His youngest son, James (1739–1807), founded a dynasty in which successive generations were prominent in local administration and in the legal profession, *inter alia* as solicitors to the university. Two members of this branch of the family married the daughters of college presidents and in the twentieth century Philip Morrell, Liberal M.P. for South Oxfordshire, and his wife, Lady Ottoline, sister of the Duke of Portland, became known as regular entertainers of various literary figures at their home, Garsington Manor. One of Jeremiah's other sons, Mark (1737–87), together with his son, James (died 1855), entered the brewing business in the town in the late eighteenth century as partners of the Tawneys. James Morrell was thus enabled to acquire Headington Hill Hall which remained in the family's possession until sold to the city in 1953. Morrell's brewery, housed in the Lion Brewery in St. Thomas's Street, probably established in 1782, is one of the few remaining old-established family brewery firms in the country, having been

119   An Oxford book auction in 1747: painting by W. Green.

A Gold Coast Tribute to a 1931 Outfit.

Gold Coast   April 1933

Walters on the Eleventh Parallel

Dear Sirs You may find the accompanying Snapshot of interest do what you like with it. This is a part of your Outfit on a cross-country trek quite near the Eleventh Parallel of Latitude.   Yours faithfully.

127   Oxford tailoring goes abroad.

managed by the family directly until 1863, by trustees for their benefit until 1943, and since then by a private limited liability company under the family's control. The trustees' minute books record decisions taken not only about the brewery but about its many local public houses. On 14 October 1914 the trustees decided that the war with Germany obliged them to alter the name of *The King of Prussia* public house at Rose Hill, shown here in a photograph taken in about 1910, to *The Allied Arms*. When it was known as *The Allied Arms* the sign was redesigned several times: one of the designs in 1938 incorporated, somewhat oddly, three sportsmen. The house is now known as *The Ox*.

Morrell's Brewery
OCL Photo 75/5029
OCL Photo 12799

[49]

126–7

The Oxford tailor in the wider world

The historic importance of tailors in Oxford and their role as credit financiers to generations of university men is evident from earlier items. In the nineteenth and twentieth centuries some made a speciality of fitting out those Oxford men who were undergoing training to administer the empire and the colonies both at the Indian Institute and, subsequently, by way of the colonial service course. Walters and Co. (Oxford) Ltd., a firm in existence from about 1886, specialized in this side of the business in the 1920s and 1930s while also leading the way in domestic fashions such as the famous 'Oxford bags'. Two photographs show the firm's overseas trade in operation. One shows a cart standing outside the Turl Street shop in the 1920s laden with equipment to be taken to the railway station for transport to the appropriate port. The other, sent to the firm by a grateful customer in 1933, shows part of a Walters outfit on safari in West Africa.

Walters and Co. (Oxford) Ltd.

128–9

An Oxford builder in the twentieth century

Just as the construction of the great college and university buildings in the earlier centuries provided much work for leading stonemasons and builders, so their maintenance and reconstruction in this century have made household names of Oxford building firms. The development of the city as an industrial centre, too, has led to a demand for the skills of the builder in both factory and house-building. One firm which has responded to all these needs is that which grew up after two carpenters, George Benfield and W. F. Loxley, went into partnership in 1876. Their first big job was to build Magdalen College School House next to Magdalen Bridge, and since then, many of the major twentieth-century Oxford buildings, the New Bodleian amongst them, have been erected by them. Virtually the entire Cowley works is of their construction. A pamphlet produced in 1951 highlights their work on the Kiln Lane estate, one of those built to cater for the needs of people drawn to Oxford by the expanding Morris Motors and Pressed Steel factories.

Between 1900 and 1915 the firm had its own brickworks at Sandford-on-Thames with what in 1900 was the biggest brick-kiln in the world. Part of its labour force was employed in making sandstock bricks by hand, each impressed with the firm's name.

Benfield & Loxley Ltd.

130–1

College servants

The colleges have over the years provided a steady source of employment for townsmen and towns-women. From the earliest days there has been a need for cooks, butlers, porters, scouts, laundresses, gardeners, and messengers as well as for hosts of maintenance men. Though the financial rewards have not always been as great as those to be obtained in other jobs, nevertheless whole dynasties of college servants have grown up with strong loyalties to particular colleges. It is interesting that figures provided by the 1851 census show that 27 per cent of those employed in the city of Oxford were engaged in domestic service, which compares with an average for England and Wales of 13 per cent.

The view of Christ Church kitchen which appeared in Rudolph Ackermann's *History of Oxford* (1814) shows the working conditions of the cooks and kitchen-workers at that time. The photograph is of a group of Brasenose College servants taken in 1861 in the college's front quadrangle (the statue has long since been removed).

Exeter College copy of Ackermann
Brasenose College photograph

Public services and social activities

Relations between town and gown have undergone many vicissitudes, but their mutual interdependence has forged many links. As a result of the growth of the university within the city there were, before the latter part of the nineteenth century, to all intents and purposes, two local authorities, and public services introduced by one almost automatically conferred benefits on the other. In the field of transport the two groups of consumers were drawn together by a shared interest in obtaining adequate services, cheaper goods and fuel. Even the university's early opposition to the railways was echoed, though for different reasons, by the city. University recreation created public walks and provided spectator sports of all kinds, while the very existence of the historic university and college buildings has attracted, over the last two centuries, an increasing number of tourists who have brought their custom to the city's inns, hotels, cafés and shops. Support from city and university led to the building of the New Theatre in 1886, and the university now owns the Playhouse. Oxford has for centuries been a very musical town and the flourishing musical societies which grew up over the last century and a half have welcomed both city residents and members of the university. Links between town and gown have, finally, been evident in the sphere of education, where the contribution of the university to elementary, secondary and adult education within the city has been of great significance.

132–3

Water supply

An engraving of 1755 by J. Donowell shows the view down St. Aldate's from Carfax at that date. On the left are the nine arches of the old town hall, opened in 1753 and pulled down in 1892–3 (see nos. 69–71), and on the right the butter market or butter bench and the east end of St. Martin's Church with one of the quarter boys visible. Only the west front of Christ Church with the familiar outline of Tom Tower remains recognizable today. To the left of the picture but in the centre of the Carfax crossing stood the great conduit, the construction of which was financed by Otho Nicholson, a wealthy London lawyer, between 1615 and 1617. This contained the cisterns to which water was conveyed from a well-house above North Hinksey and pumped into the cisterns through the carved body of an ox. This arrangement and some of the elaborate decoration of the conduit was frankly described in a little manuscript written at about the time that Donowell was making the engraving but evidently copying an earlier description. The upper cistern supplied water to the colleges and some private houses. Townspeople were able to collect water from the lower cistern and it was this outlet which was made to flow with wine on great feast days. The conduit was removed as a traffic obstruction in 1787, by which time the works were controlled by the university. The town had established its own waterworks at Folly Bridge in 1694, and eventually in 1869 purchased the university system.

Bodl. Gough Maps 27, no.31
Bodl. MS.Top.Oxon. e.6

134-5

Street-lighting

A university pamphleteer argued in 1764 that poor street-lighting was the result of the townsmen's false belief that lamps served only to light drunken gownsmen home. By way of reply, 'A Citizen' argued in *A Candid remonstrance to the Vice-Chancellor* . . . that lighting in the town was much superior to that for which the university was responsible. This difference of opinion serves to illustrate that responsibility for lighting the streets was divided. In 1614 the council had ordered freemen to hang lanterns outside their doors from 6 p.m. to 9 p.m. between 1 November and 2 February. The university made similar orders for the lighting of colleges and the houses of privileged persons in 1636. Some responsibility for street-lighting passed to the parishes in the late seventeenth century, and they supplied lamps and paid for their upkeep for much of the eighteenth century. A sub-committee of the Paving Commissioners assumed responsibility in 1773, raising and spending a special lighting rate. Gas lighting was introduced in 1819, and by 1833 there were 225 gas lamps. Electric street-lighting,

powered from the Osney works of the Oxford Electric Company Ltd., gradually replaced gas from 1892. The benefits which the activities of the Osney works conferred on Oxford were celebrated in a spoof entry for the Newdigate Prize by Hilaire Belloc. It was not, however, until 1979 that the last gas lamp in Oxford was taken out of use.

Bodl. G.A.Oxon.8° 1033(3)
Bodl. 28001 e.855

136

Street-cleansing

By the late thirteenth century the university was aware of the threat to health presented by dunghills, pigsties, and slaughter-houses within the town walls; it was able to persuade successive kings to stir the corporation to action and, after the St. Scholastica's Day riot of 1355, assumed general control of the streets (see no. 39). The exact division of responsibility between corporation and university remained a subject of continued dispute, since both bodies held leets at which street offenders were arraigned (see no. 84). In practice, the university seems to have had power to compel the cleansing or repair of the streets only if the corporation had failed to act. During the eighteenth century the corporation took so little part in street-cleansing that the university leet roll of 1733 shows it being prosecuted in its own guild hall for a large dunghill in the old Butcher Row (Queen Street). On the same occasion, Jesus College was fined 6s. 8d. for allowing 'a necessary house' within the college walls to become a great nuisance to 'his Majesty's Liege Subjects passing that way'.

OUA WPβ/Q/16

137-8

University lodging-houses

The rapid expansion of the university in the second half of the nineteenth century meant that many more undergraduates were arriving than the colleges had accommodation for within their walls. The University Lodging-House Delegacy was therefore formed in 1868 to license and supervise lodging-houses for them. By 1879 some 579 lodging-houses had been licensed and the lodging-house keeper or landlady had become a feature of

Oxford life. In December 1880 an undergraduate lodger died of diphtheria, and this caused the Delegacy to tighten up the licensing procedures. The houses of all applicants for a licence were inspected by the Delegacy sanitary officer, and detailed reports were produced such as this one for 29 Holywell, made in 1885 and 1886. All sanitary defects had to be corrected if the licence was to be kept, and improvements were therefore made to many houses in the town. The reports provide for historians a most valuable survey of living conditions in parts of later nineteenth-century Oxford, but when they were made they provoked a sharp reaction from the city authorities, who claimed that the university had no authority to lay down sanitary conditions for town properties. The dispute, however, led to the introduction of stringent drainage by-laws by the Oxford Local Board in 1889.

There were those, such as Dean Burgon, who were opposed to the whole idea of lodging-houses for undergraduates. His arguments, expressed in a pamphlet entitled *Our present lodging-house system immoral: and requiring reform* (1876) were mainly concerned with the moral dangers to which serving-girls were likely to be exposed.

OUA LHD/SF/2/1
OUA LHD/RP/2/16

139

The University Parks

The Parks had been in use for recreational purposes since at least the seventeenth century but were greatly extended after their acquisition by the university in 1854 (see nos. 12–13). In the later nineteenth century they became a fashionable resort for Sunday promenades, while during the week they were thronged with nursemaids and perambulators.

The Curators of the Parks received applications for all sorts of activities to take place there. At their meeting on 26 June 1900 they gave permission for the Oxford City Volunteer Corps to drill in the Parks, so long as they kept to the Rugby Football Ground; for the City Tourist Committee's band to play there during the Long Vacation; and for the Revd G. Simeon and Mr Festing to wheel their tricycles as far as the Cricket Ground provided that they did not ride them.

OUA WPβ/20/4, fol.82

140

Fire-brigade

A fragmentary fire-service existed in early nineteenth-century Oxford with engines owned, for example, by some colleges and parishes, but the university resolved in 1809 to establish a regular, though part-time, fire-brigade, as recorded here in the Water and Fire Tax accounts. The university's fire-engine was first used in 1810 at a fire on Captain Nowell's premises at Iffley. Although the need for a separate force was diminished by the formation of the Oxford Volunteer Fire Brigade in 1870, the university's uniformed firemen remained active until the 1880s. From 1820, the money raised by the university firebox was also used to provide life-saving apparatus on the river Thames in Oxford.

OUA WPα/56/7

141

Carrying services

The university established a system of carrying by the end of the Middle Ages, and in 1448 it was agreed that university carriers should be included amongst the privileged persons of the university. The sole right of licensing carriers was claimed by the university but, in the sixteenth century at least, the city also appointed them. University carriers were expected to maintain high standards in return for monopoly status on their route. In two documents of 1678, Thomas Bew, who lived at The Oranges and Lemons opposite Magdalen College, agreed to maintain hackney horses in Oxford and London and to make two journeys each way every week, giving preference to scholars and privileged persons at all times.

OUA CC/134/2/2

142

Stage-coaches

As with carrying services, the university claimed the sole right to license coaches staging in Oxford, and in 1667 a stage-coach was providing three journeys a week to London. By 1669 proprietors undertook to complete the journey in one thirteen-hour day during the summer. In this printed notice dated 1720, William Haynes advertised four trips to London each week, of which one at least completed the journey in a day. His advertisement stressed that he had the university licence. Oxford gradually became a major coaching centre, and services to Bath and Bristol were established in 1702, to Gloucester by 1713, and to Birmingham, Hereford, Warwick, and Worcester by 1753. By the early nineteenth century the university had ceased to exercise the licensing right, deterred, perhaps, by the scale of the traffic.

OUA CC/134/2/2

143

River navigation

An Act of 1623 authorized the appointment of eight commissioners of rivers, also known as the Oxford–Burcot Commission, comprising four city and four university representatives, with powers to cleanse the river Thames and to reinstate the navigation between Burcot, near Dorchester, and Oxford. Pound locks, then known as turnpikes, were built at Culham, Sandford, and Iffley, and the first barge reached Oxford in 1635. Ordinary commerce suffered during the Civil War, but an active traffic in stone, timber, coal, potash, malt, and foodstuffs was resumed in the later seventeenth and early eighteenth centuries. It was important to both city and university that the river should remain navigable, and the commissioners' account book in 1651 records substantial payments by both bodies for work on the lock at Swift Ditch, near Abingdon, by Thomas Wicks. The minute was written by Gerard Langbaine, Keeper of the University Archives, and signed by him together with John Saunders, Provost of Oriel, and three city aldermen, Henry Sowtham, Martin Wright, and Humfrey Whistler.

OCRO CH.N.IX/i, fols.6ᵛ–7

144

The canal

A canal linking Oxford with the Coventry canal was proposed at a public meeting in Banbury in 1768. It eventually reached Oxford on 1 January 1790 when the first boats entered the New Road wharves. For a short time thereafter Oxford became a junction on the shortest route by water between the Midlands and London, and commodities, particularly coals, could be brought to the city at a much cheaper rate. From the beginning Oxford inhabitants, and particularly members of the university, were prominent among the company's shareholders and on the board of management which until 1885 was headed by 'an ordained chairman'. The fortunes of the canal fluctuated over the next century, much long-distance haulage falling first to other canals and then to the railways. The real decline in traffic came in the twentieth century with the advance of road haulage, however, and the southern section of the canal was closed in 1955.

At the period when there was a great deal of traffic on the canal, a floating chapel was provided in Oxford at the expense of Mr Ward, a coal merchant, for the bargemen and their families. It also served as a schoolroom for their children. Designed by John Plowman and consecrated in 1839, it floated on the canal just north of Hythe Bridge. This photograph was taken in about 1860 and shows both the chapel and the old bridge which was replaced in 1861. The chapel unfortunately sank in about 1868 and a new chapel and schoolroom, built on dry land in Hythe Bridge Street, replaced it.

Bodl. MS.Top.Oxon.d.505, fol.274

145

Railways

The city objected consistently to early railway schemes because it feared that easy access to London would rob local traders of much of their business, especially with colleges. The university's main doubt lay with the effects of the railway upon discipline, but this petition to parliament in 1838, apparently drawn up by Thomas Gaisford, Dean of Christ Church and Regius Professor of Greek, and annotated by a contemporary as 'a model for plain good sense', stressed also that the proposed scheme was premature, unnecessary, and posed threats of flooding. The combined opposition of leading landowners, the university, and the city was sufficient to defeat proposals in 1837, 1838 and 1840, but the city was virtually alone in opposing the successful Oxford Railway Company scheme of 1843. The university was won over by provisions that gave

144   The floating chapel on the canal.

university officials access to all stations and the right to demand information concerning any passenger suspected of being a member of the university. The line from Didcot to Oxford was opened on 12 June 1844 with a station to the south-west of Folly Bridge.

OUA WPγ/22/1/s

146

Horse-trams

The City of Oxford & District Tramways Co. was incorporated in 1879, and opened its first line between the stations and Magdalen Road on 1 December 1881. It was promoted primarily to cater for suburban residents and people travelling to and from the railway stations, but members of the university were always seen as potential patrons. This cartoon, published photographically in 1878, envisaged a university service, offering $1\frac{1}{2}d$. fares to

the Oxford Union and half-price reductions to undergraduates going unwillingly to the Examination Schools. Some opposition to the tramway was inevitable, and 'B', writing in the *Undergraduate's Journal*, complained of the company's 'iron grasp upon the "High" '. Fears of distracting noise led the university to insist that the tram-road outside the Examination Schools should be laid with wood blocks rather than granite setts.

Bodl. G.A.Oxon.4° 414, no.536

147

Horse-racing

Port Meadow formed the venue for Oxford race-meetings between 1630 and 1880, and Benjamin Cole's map of *c.*1720 illustrates the two-mile pear-shaped course used until 1848. The meetings were generally held in late August, and in 1710 included sideshows, beer-stalls, and foot-races. There were

I.Donowell Arch. del. A View of the Conduit (a) part of Carfax Church (b), the Piazza called the
Butter Market (c), the Town Hall (d), the west: Front of Christ Church College (e), &c. in the
University of OXFORD. Published according to Act of Parliament Feb: 1755 &c

132   View from Carfax down St. Aldate's, 1755.

Veüe du Conduit (a) *, d'une partie de l'Eglise de Carfax* (b) *, du Piazza qu'on appelle le Marché au Beurre* (c) *, de la Maison de Ville* (d) *, de la Façade a l'ouest du College de l'Eglise de Christ* (e) *, &c. dans l'Université d'*OXFORD.

t the Golden Lion in Fleetstreet, London.

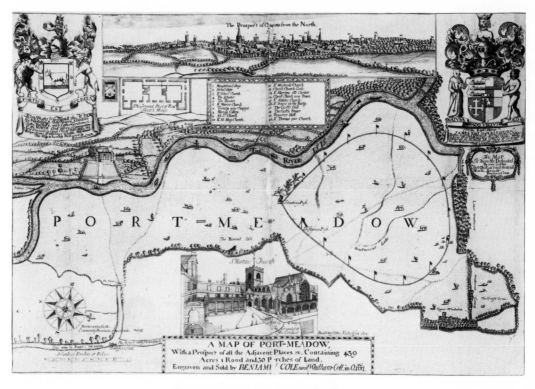

147   The race-course on Port Meadow, *c.*1720.

also smock-races in which the women wore petti-
coats and low-necked shifts and men breeches
without shirts. By 1722 the university felt bound to
legislate against members' involvement in horse-
racing. The fashionable status of the meeting
diminished in the nineteenth century and, eventually, financial difficulties and a long-standing
dispute with Oxford freemen over the right to use
Port Meadow caused the race committee to aban-
don the meeting after 1880. Races were revived in
1980, after a lapse of 100 years. Cole's map carries
incidental illustrations of Carfax and of Benjamin
Swete's new manor house at Medley, as well as a
fine prospect of the city from the north.

Bodl. Gough maps 27, no.104

148–9

Vaulting, dancing, and fencing schools

William Stokes's book *The vaulting master, or the art
of vaulting* was published in 1641, and served as an
illustrated guide to that popular mid-seventeenth-
century recreation. Stokes hoped that the exercise
would enable men to achieve bodily fitness and to
avoid the base idleness 'that has shrunk mens
sinews, and enfeebled them, even to the contempt of
beasts'. From *c.*1621 he ran a dancing and vaulting
school on the first floor of a house in Cornmarket
Street just outside the North Gate. His pupils
included the diarist John Evelyn, and the dramatist
William Cartwright. Prince Charles, later Charles
II, attended the school in 1642–3, but Stokes was
by this time suffering from failing health and died in
August 1643. The school had apparently been
started by John Bossely earlier in the century and
continued until about 1690. The 'pass' illustrated
here was one of the more complicated ones
designed to excite 'the admiration of the beholders'.

Dancing was taught not only with vaulting but
also with fencing. John Earle, tutor to Prince
Charles, doubtless had his tongue in his cheek
when writing in his *Microcosmographie* (1628) that
a university should be judged on the quality of its
fencing and dancing schools. In the early nineteenth century a fashionable fencing school was

run by Henry Angelo, one of a dynasty of fencing-masters. A copy of his father's textbook on the subject, *L'Ecole d'armes* published in 1765, contains a list of those undergraduates (many of them titled) who were enrolled in the Oxford class of February 1806.

Bodl. 8°A 29 Art.BS.
Bodl. MS.Top.Oxon.b.269

150–1

Rowing

Rowing at Oxford was originally indulged in for air and exercise, and eight-oared racing was not recorded before 1815. The Eights were at first rowed in top hats, and some coxswains continued to wear them until the formation of the Oxford University Boat Club in 1839. The races attracted little attention even in local newspapers until the later 1830s, when they became designated as 'those manly and noble sports'. By the end of the nineteenth century Eights Week was immensely popular, and photographs show great crowds in punts, on college barges, and on the towpath. The production of charts for Eights Week developed into a considerable seasonal industry. The growth of university rowing probably encouraged parallel developments in the city, and the City of Oxford Regatta was first held in 1841.

OCL Photo 4171
Bodl. John Johnson Collection, Sports 13

148   Vaulting as practised at W. Stokes's dancing and vaulting school, 1620s.

152

A landmark for walkers

There have always been those — members of the university or townsmen — who have preferred the pleasures of walking to the more energetic pursuit of organized team sports. Walking does not need the creation of playing fields for its enjoyment although special 'Constitutional Walks' alongside the Banbury, Woodstock and Iffley Roads were laid out by public subscription in 1820. It does, however, lead to the creation of particular landmarks such as Joe Pullen's Tree, a gigantic elm tree at the top of Headington Hill to which Josiah Pullen, the vice-principal of Magdalen Hall who died in 1714, was reputed to walk twice a day. The engraving of a sketch by Mrs J. Wright in 1847 shows the tree with a woodman at its foot. The tree survived various assaults from the axe but was eventually destroyed by fire in 1908.

OCL Illustration 3003

153–6

The theatre

Fearing the distraction of scholars by 'bad persons', the university had forbidden performances by common players within the city of Oxford in 1584. Professional companies continued to visit Oxford during the week of the University Act in July, and Shakespeare's own company, the King's Players, came to the city six times between 1604 and 1613. Nevertheless, it was not until the 1880s that the staging of plays during term-time was allowed. Plays were performed during the vacation, but during university terms earlier in the nineteenth century any theatrical performance had to masquerade as a concert. A theatre, called the New Theatre, was opened in St. Mary's Hall Lane, Oriel Street, in 1833 when an address in rhyming couplets was declaimed. This building was replaced in 1836 by a second New Theatre, built in a court off George Street. It was also known as the Victoria Theatre after the name of the court in which it was situated, and later as the Theatre Royal after the name of the company which played there. With support from university circles, and notably from Benjamin Jowett, Master of Balliol, as well as townspeople, the Victoria was replaced by another New Theatre in 1886. Edward Rose's touring company, visiting the theatre in Commemoration Week 1886, soon after its reopening, included a new one-act play 'The Girl Graduate' written specially for the occasion. The building was greatly altered in 1905 and continued in use until it was demolished and rebuilt in 1933–4. Its name was changed to The Apollo in 1981.

The Playhouse began in 1923 as a repertory theatre in the old Red Barn, a former Big Game Museum in the Woodstock Road, and issued an appeal to the university and the city to support the attempt 'to raise the standard of the acted drama in England'. The list of signatories was an impressive one. The present Oxford Playhouse was built in Beaumont Street in 1938. The lease was purchased by the university with the help of the University Grants Committee in 1961.

OCL OXFO 792 PLAY & NEW
Bodl. M. adds.129 b.11
Bodl. M. adds.129 b.9

157

Theatrical licensing

The vice-chancellor still has the right to veto any public performance. In previous centuries his active consent was necessary and the proctors kept an alphabetical register of entertainments licensed. The page shown covers performances ranging from *Lady Windermere's Fan* to Lord George Sanger's circus. *Little Miss Nobody* which was performed at the New Theatre in May 1899 evidently caused problems. The show girls fraternized too much with members of the university and the play was considered 'not decent'.

OUA Proctors' records

158–62

Music: singing and performing

Musical societies and the concerts which they give have for centuries provided a powerful bond between all the inhabitants of Oxford. The nineteenth and twentieth centuries have seen many new societies formed in an area of artistic endeavour in which Oxford has always been strong, The origins of the Oxford Bach Choir, for instance, who are shown here singing Bach's 'B Minor Mass' in

163   The Electra Palace cinema.

the Sheldonian Theatre in May 1935, go back to
1896 when their first conductor was Dr Basil
Harwood, organist at Christ Church. In 1901 he
was succeeded by Dr (later Sir) Hugh Allen who in
the same year had taken over the conductorship of
the Oxford Choral and Philharmonic Society. This
society arose from an amalgamation in 1890 of the
Oxford Choral Society, founded in 1819, and the
Oxford Philharmonic Society, founded by Sir John
Stainer in 1865. Members' tickets are shown for the
year before and the year after the amalgamation,
together with an announcement of the Choral
Society's performance of the 'Messiah' at Christmas
1869 and the programme of a concert in November
1881 at which Arthur Sullivan conducted his own
'The Martyr of Antioch'. Under Hugh Allen the
Choral and Philharmonic Society was merged with
the Bach Choir.

Allen was also one of those primarily responsible
for starting the Oxford Subscription Concerts and
he chaired a meeting on 11 January 1920 'to
consider what may be done by means of united
action on the part of musical societies and individuals to promote the performance of good music in
Oxford'. The first of the resulting concerts, guaran-
teed by subscription, was given on 21 October of

that year. Allen himself conducted. Myra Hess was
the pianist, and the programme included the first
performance of Parry's 'An English Suite in G for
Strings' as well as a piece by George Butterworth
who had been killed in World War I. Like all the
early subscription concerts it was held on a Thurs-
day afternoon, a time judged convenient for Oxford
dons, business people (it was early closing day), and
country subscribers. The Bach Choir and the
Subscription Concerts still flourish vigorously.

OCL Photo 75/5400
Bodl. MS.Top.Oxon.d.483, fols.1ᵛ–2, 95ᵛ
Bodl. G.A.Oxon.4° 609
Bodl. MS.Top.Oxon.c.677/1, fol.3

163–4

Cinemas

The Electra Palace in Queen Street was opened on
25 March 1911, and the photograph shows the
outside of Oxford's first large and luxurious cinema,
designed to show films for a more adult and
informed audience. 'The Three Musketeers' was
showing there in November 1913. Beneath a

placard giving opening times, a notice advised that members of the university would be admitted only to the most expensive seats, those costing 1s. This message, backed up by uniformed attendants, doubtless sought to deter the kind of rowdyism which had long been practised by some undergraduates at plays and concerts. In the longer term, Oxford student life had a much more positive effect upon local cinemas, ensuring a good audience for quality films and helping some cinemas to stay in business or even to reopen after closure.

OCL Photo 81/1221
Bodl. John Johnson Collection, Cinema 5 (2 items)

165

College schools

The three most ancient schools for children which still exist in Oxford are all closely tied to colleges. New College provided for its boy-choristers from its origins in 1379, and the provision of a choir for the cathedral was the main reason for the foundation of Christ Church Cathedral School in 1546. They are now independent preparatory schools, though both have at various times over the centuries aimed to rival Magdalen College School in providing the facilities of a grammar school. Magdalen College School was founded in 1480 and has played a continuously important part in the educational life of the city since that date. One of its early schoolmasters was John Stanbridge, whose *Accidence* (c. 1510) — a book used to teach pupils the rudiments of Latin — shows a group of pupils sitting before their master.

Bodl. 4° A 18 Art. BS.

166–7

Charity schools

A number of charity schools have existed in the city. The longest-lived was Nixon's School which was founded in 1658 and lasted until 1885. Its school building, in a yard behind the old town hall, was demolished when the site for the new town hall was cleared in 1892. Combe's School in St. Thomas's parish (founded in 1702), the Bluecoat Schools for boys and girls originally in St.

Martin's parish (founded in 1708), and Alworth's School in St. Michael's parish (founded in 1721) all came to an end in the nineteenth century. All had been supported from funds within the town or the county, and indeed Alderman John Nixon's foundation specifically excluded all boys whose fathers served the university in any capacity. One charity school was founded in 1708 by a group of university men headed by the vice-chancellor. This was Greycoat School which began life in the parish of St. Peter in the East and after several moves settled in Great Clarendon Street. By 1865 the growth of parochial schools had diminished the need for this school and it was closed. The boys, who wore grey clothes, were given a basic education and apprenticeships were sought for them. The accounts for the years 1831–2 show receipts of £661 5s. 0d. and sundry disbursements. Clothing for the year cost £127 and apprenticeship premiums for nine boys cost £180. The indentures for William Shurrock, one of the boys apprenticed in that year, show that he was bound for seven years to George Gardiner, a tailor in St. Ebbe's.

OUA MR/4/2/7,21

168–9

City of Oxford High School for Boys

In the 1870s the city authorities perceived the need for a new grammar school. Nixon's School for the sons of freemen was in decline, the Bluecoat School had insufficient means, the two college schools of Christ Church and New College were primarily schools for choristers, and Magdalen College School had insufficient accommodation for day scholars to cater for the growing middle classes in the city. An appeal was therefore launched, and a site was given by the corporation between New Inn Hall Street and George Street. The university, the colleges, and individuals responded generously to the appeal both for the provision of buildings and for endowment. The school, in the handsome building designed by T. G. Jackson, opened in 1881 and scholarships were available from the earliest years. The school has had a very successful subsequent history. It merged with Southfield School in 1966 to form Oxford School and vacated the Jackson buildings, which now house the university Social Studies Faculty centre.

Bodl. G.A.Oxon.b.160, fols.22 and 35

170–1

Oxford High School for Girls

The Oxford High School for Girls opened in 1875 in the Judge's Lodgings in St. Giles under the auspices of the Girls' Public Day School Trust. Since then it has moved from St. Giles to the Banbury Road and, in 1957, to Belbroughton Road. It has built one of the highest academic records in the country, and at the start of the 1981–2 school year had 583 pupils. The school has always had a fine musical tradition and the list of fees for additional subjects in 1906 reflects this. The first issue of the school magazine *Ad Lucem* contained an article 'Behaviour in the street' which reported some of the early criticisms levelled against this new girls' school.

Bodl. Per.G.A.Oxon. 8° 612
Bodl. G.A.Oxon.b.160, fol.40

172

Parish schools

Parochial schools were established in most Oxford parishes from the 1830s, and the principle of a voluntary school supported by the generosity and religious zeal of its parishioners spread quickly to the city's newer suburbs. Colleges were substantial landowners in most suburban parishes, and were often prepared to grant sites for these schools. In the case of Summertown, St. John's College gave a site adjoining St. John's Church in Church Street, now Rogers Street, and a day- and Sunday-school was built there in 1848. The college also supplemented the school's income by an annual grant. The school was enlarged in 1867, 1872, 1887 and 1909, but it closed in 1964 and was subsequently demolished. This photograph of the pupils at Summertown Infants' School was taken in 1876. A none-too-serious attempt has apparently been made to identify the boys in the back row as Lord S, Viscount P, Duke of B, Sir George, etc.

OCL Photo 78/5644

173

Adult education

The provision by the university of teaching for adult students who could not enter the university was begun by Oxford in 1878, five years after a similar scheme had been inaugurated by Cambridge. The administration was at first entrusted to a special committee of the Delegacy of Local Examinations, but, as the work expanded, it was transferred in 1892 to the control of a new delegacy 'for the extension of teaching beyond the limits of the University'. In the early days extension teaching consisted of courses of lectures, sometimes to as many as 1,000 people, each of which was preceded or followed by a class. After each lecture members of the audience would take away questions for written work and, at the end of the course, assiduous students could sit an examination for a terminal or sessional certificate. One such student was Mrs Lydia Blackwell, mother of Sir Basil Blackwell, who obtained a terminal certificate in 1886 after attending a course on English History 1760–1815.

Lent by Frank Pickstock, Esq.

Historical notes on some of the sponsors

BBC Radio Oxford

Opened 29 October 1970; provides news, information, discussion, education and entertainment for Oxfordshire.

Art Needlework Industries Limited

Established in Königsberg 1901, moved to London 1933, premises there destroyed by bombing in war. Moved to Oxford, in premises leased from Jesus College. Proprietor has published works on handicrafts, especially knitting and embroidery.

Barclays Bank Limited, Old Bank

The Old Bank began during the late eighteenth century as an offshoot of the partnership of William Fletcher and John Parsons, mercers. The Thomson family became involved during the early nineteenth century; amalgamation with Barclays Bank took place in 1900.

B. H. Blackwell Limited

Benjamin Henry Blackwell opened a bookshop at 50 Broad Street, on 1 January 1879. Subsequently nos. 51, 48 and 49 were added. Basil (now Sir Basil) joined his father shortly before World War I. Publishing activities were begun in 1880. Today two-thirds of the books sold go overseas.

British Rail, Oxford Area

Proposals from 1833 onwards for a rail link to Oxford were opposed by both city and university. First station opened in 1844 at Folly Bridge, present station in 1852.

British Telecommunications

First telephone exchange in Oxford opened in 1886 by South of England Telephone Company. It was taken over in 1890 by National Telephone Company and by the Post Office in 1912. Now British Telecom, with main office in Paradise Street.

Buckell & Ballard

Established 1887 by Robert Buckell, who was later knighted and was mayor six times. In World War II made priced inventory of Oxford Corporation possessions.

City of Oxford Taxicab Association

Formed in 1954. Horse-drawn carriages were not completely replaced by motor-cars until mid-1930s.

Frank Cooper

Cooper's Oxford marmalade first made by Frank's wife in 1874 in the old Angel Hotel; in 1902 moved to Victoria Buildings near the station. Product known internationally. Firm now part of multinational company.

E. H. Crapper Esq.

Crapper family businesses have served city and university since Noah, a cordwainer, became a freeman of the city in 1701.

Gill & Co. (Ironmongers) Limited

Earliest known owners of the ironmongery (1530) were the Smythe family. Several members became mayor, and there were connections with William Smith, Bishop of Lincoln, who founded Brasenose College.

Halls Oxford & West Brewery Company Limited

Halls Oxford Brewery Limited founded at the Swan Brewery, Paradise Street, by Squire Hall in 1896. The Eagle Brewery (Weaving & Son) and City Brewery (Hanley Bros) were later acquired. Present company extends from Oxford to Cornwall.

G. T. Jones & Co.

Established 1787. Shippers of wine to university and the city corporation. Originally occupied cellars of the earlier Swindlestock Tavern at Carfax.

Mallams

Auctioneers, founded in 1788 by James Mallam, solicitor and estate agent.

Morrells' Brewery Limited

The only surviving brewery in the city, some five hundred years old, has belonged to the Morrell family for about two hundred years. Still independent, it supplies many college common rooms and its own 140 houses in the city and surroundings.

A. R. Mowbray & Co. Limited

Religious bookselling business founded at no. 2 Cornmarket by A. R. Mowbray in 1858, now serves the whole Anglican Communion. Has publishing division, situated next to St. Thomas's Church where the founder sang in the choir.

Payne & Son (Goldsmiths) Limited

Founded at Wallingford in 1790, it moved to Oxford in 1888, and still occupies the same premises in High Street. Has supplied many presentation silver pieces to city, university and colleges, and made a copy of the Alfred Jewel for the Ashmolean Museum.

Post Office, Oxford

Present main office in St. Aldate's was opened in 1881. Some sixty years earlier there were four members of staff, for a population of 15,000. Now there are some 1,000, with 300 offices to man and 3 million letters a week to be handled.

Savory's

This tobacconist firm, originally the Oxford branch of the London company H. L. Savory & Co. Ltd. but now owned by Ward's Tobacconists Ltd., trades from picturesque premises in High Street which have figured in records of Oxford from 1297.

Shepherd & Woodward Limited

This firm of city and university men's outfitters and robemakers dates in origin from 1863 when Mr G. Brockington opened a journeyman tailoring business. Bought in 1877 by Mr A. Shepherd and amalgamated with Wilton Woodward tailors in 1927, the business moved from Cornmarket to its present High Street site.

Stephenson & Co. (Oxford) Limited

William Stephenson set up as a coal and builders' merchant in 1876, and moved to Juxon Street by 1879. He prospered during the great building developments in North Oxford when fellows of colleges were allowed to marry. A private company with the above name was registered in 1912. When it moved to the present Botley Road site in the mid-30s, earth required to raise the ground level was brought from the Broad Street excavation just beginning on the New Bodleian site.

Symm & Co. Limited

Founded in early nineteenth century by Josiah Symm, a Scotsman, in Little Clarendon Street. Major building work, for example on Exeter College Chapel, Indian Institute, Christ Church Meadow Building, and currently Magdalen College Tower and Wolsey Tower, and Merton College chapel tower and east window.

Thornton Baker

Chartered accountants, previously Thornton & Thornton, founded in 1904 by R. W. Thornton, son of J. H. Thornton, the Broad Street bookseller. Acted for William Morris (later Lord Nuffield) in his business and charitable concerns, and does so for some colleges.

Walters & Co. (Oxford) Limited

Established 1886, men's outfitters to city and university. Renowned for 'Oxford bags'.

Christ Church Cathedral School

In 1546 provision was made for the education of eight choristers on King Henry VIII's foundation of the Cathedral and College of Christ Church. It is now a preparatory school taking non-choristers as well, and numbers one hundred.

Magdalen College School

William of Waynflete provided in his foundation (1448) for sixteen choristers. The school, which dates its origin from 1480, was situated within the college precincts until 1928, when it was moved to its present site. Open from the start to non-members of the college, it has always had strong links with both city and university. Choristers sing from the tower on May Morning.

New College School

Founding the college in 1379, William of Wykeham provided for the education of sixteen choristers. The school was accommodated first in the undercroft, then in other parts of the college and its immediate vicinity. The present school in Savile Road dates from 1903. Non-choristers were probably not admitted until the mid-seventeenth century.